MILITARY AVIATION LIBRARY
World War II

German Aircraft

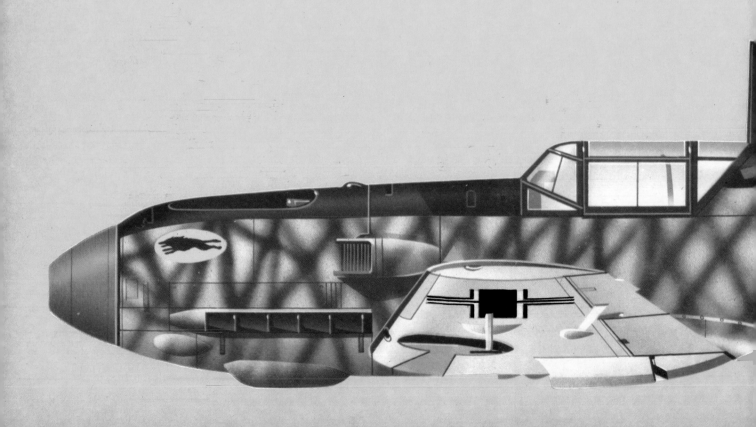

MILITARY AVIATION LIBRARY
World War II
German Aircraft

Bill Gunston

CHARTWELL
BOOKS, INC.

Published by Chartwell Books Inc., New York

©Salamander Books Ltd., 1985

Colour profiles, cutaways and three-view drawings © Pilot Press Ltd.

ISBN: 0 89009 900 6

PICTURE CREDITS

Bapty & Co: 31, 45 (bottom), 48 (left).
Dornier-Pressestelle: 18 (centre).
Fokker-VFW: 20 (bottom).
Imperial War Museum: 11 (top), 33 (bottom), 44, 59 (top).
J. G. Moore Collection: 13 (centre), 14, 21, 27, 32, 37, 38, 39, 42, 49, 54, 55, 56.
Messerschmitt Archiv: 57.
Pilot Press Ltd: 8, 9, 10, 12, 13 (top and bottom), 15, 16, 17, 18 (top and
   bottom), 19, 20 (top), 22, 23, 26, 28, 29, 33 (top), 34, 35, 36, 43, 45 (top), 46,
   47, 48, (right), 50, 58, 59 (bottom), 60, 61.
Robert Hunt Library: 41.

Contents

Arado Ar 96

Ar 96A-1, Ar 96B-2 and Ar 396

Origin: Arado Flugzeugwerke; production almost entirely assigned to Ago Flugzeugwerke and to Avia and Letov in Czechoslovakia.
Type: Advanced trainer and multi-role tactical.
Engine: (96A) 240hp Argus As 10C inverted vee-8 aircooled; (B) 465hp As 410A-1 inverted vee-12 aircooled.
Dimensions: Span 36ft 1in (11·00m); length (A) 27ft 1in, (B) 29ft 11¼in (9.13m); height 8ft 6¼in (2·60m).
Weights: Empty (A) 1187lb, (B) 2,854lb (1295kg); maximum (A) 3,476lb (1577kg), (B) 3,747lb (1695kg).
Performance: Maximum speed (A, B) 205mph (330km/h); range (A) 560 miles (900km), (B) 615 miles (990km).
Armament: (A) none; (B) invariably one 7·92mm MG 17 above engine on right, sometimes 7·92mm MG 15 in rear cockpit and/or other guns in wing bulges and/or light bombs.
History: First flight 1938, (B) January 1940, final delivery (C.2B) 1948.
Users: Czechoslovakia (post-war), France (S.10), Germany, plus most other Axis air forces.

Development: Designed by Walter Blume, the Ar 96 was a typical Arado product, with distinctive tail and clean stressed-skin structure. It proved an ideal advanced trainer, and the Ar 96A entered Luftwaffe service in 1939. In 1940 much larger orders were placed for the 96B with more fuel and a larger engine, and this remained by far the most important advanced trainer of the Axis. The two-blade Argus propeller had a distinctive pitch-control windmill on the spinner, and there were five chief B sub-types of which a few could be used for gunnery and bombing training. The 96B towed light gliders, and even served in tactical roles on the Eastern front with various augmented armament. Total production by December 1944 was 11,546, and Letov built the C.2B version until 1948. The planned Ar 296 was developed into the 396, an all-wood replacement with 580hp As 411. Crude but effective, this was assigned to the French SIPA works, which after the liberation made large numbers as the S.11, followed by the metal S.12.

Right: The Ar 96B series was built in greater numbers than any other trainer in history except the American T-6 family, just topping the Vultee BT-13 Valiant family (11,537). The aircraft illustrated, probably Ar 96B-2 pilot trainers, do not bear the badge of an A/B Schule but by 1942 these were often omitted. All wartime Luftwaffe pilots knew the 96.

Arado Ar 196

Ar 196A-1 to A-5 (data for A-3)

Origin: Arado Flugzeugwerke GmbH.
Type: Two-seat maritime reconnaissance seaplane.
Engine: 960hp BMW 132K nine-cylinder radial.
Dimensions: Span 40ft 8in (12·4m); length 36ft 1in (11m); height 14ft 4½in (4·4m).
Weights: Empty 6,580lb (2990kg); loaded 8,223lb (3730kg).
Performance: Maximum speed 193mph (310km/h) at 13,120ft (4000m); initial climb 980ft (300m)/min; service ceiling 23,000ft (7020m); range 670 miles (1070km) at 158mph (253km/h).
Armament: Two MG FF 20mm cannon in wings outboard of propeller disc, one MG 17 7·92mm in top decking and twin MG 17 on pivoted mounting aimed by observer. Rack under each wing for 110lb (50kg) bomb.
History: First flight (196V1) May 1938; first operational service 1 August 1939.
Users: Bulgaria, Germany (Luftwaffe, Kriegsmarine), Romania.

Development: One of the very few float seaplanes to be used in World War II outside the Pacific area, the Ar 196 was designed as a replacement

Above: Built in small numbers in 1941, the Ar 196A-4 served on catapults of Kriegsmarine warships and preceded the A-3.

Below: By far the most numerous Ar 196 variant was the A-3, two of which are seen here flying on coastal patrol with 2/SAGr 128. This was formed in July 1943 at Brest and later moved to the south French coast where it ceased to exist.

for the He 60 biplane on the catapults of all the German Navy's capital ships. Its duties were thus primarily reconnaissance and shadowing of surface vessels, but in comparison with such Allied types as the Curtiss Seagull and Fairey Seafox it had a much higher performance and eventually was given formidable armament. Four prototypes, powered by the 880hp BMW 132Dc engine (derived in Germany from the Pratt & Whitney Hornet), were flown in 1938, two with twin floats and the others with a large central float. The following year, 26 Ar 196A-1s were built, entering service in August aboard the battle cruisers *Gneisenau* and *Scharnhorst*, and at shore bases on the North Sea. In 1940 the Ar 196A-3 entered service, and this type made up the bulk of the 401 aircraft built. Though quite outclassed by the best fighters, the A-3 was a versatile multi-role aircraft which actually spent most of the war operating on sea patrols from coastal bases, mainly on the Bay of Biscay and islands in the Mediterranean. Batches were built by Vichy-France at Saint Nazaire and, in a slightly modified A-5 form, by Fokker at Amsterdam in 1943–44. About 50 served with co-belligerent Balkan air forces in the Adriatic and Black Sea. The type was never developed as an effective anti-submarine search and strike machine, despite its obvious potential.

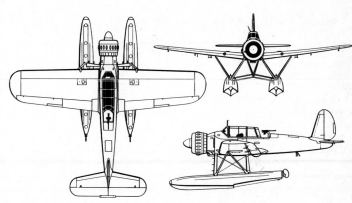

Above: Three-view of a typical Ar 196A-3.

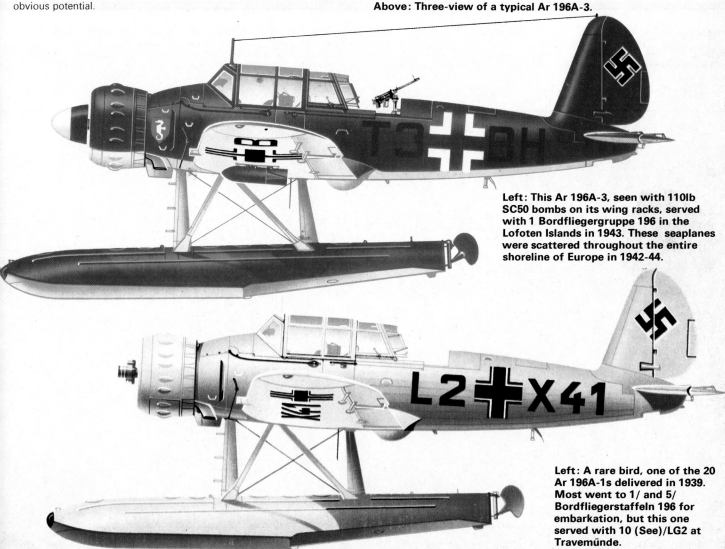

Left: This Ar 196A-3, seen with 110lb SC50 bombs on its wing racks, served with 1 Bordfliegergruppe 196 in the Lofoten Islands in 1943. These seaplanes were scattered throughout the entire shoreline of Europe in 1942-44.

Left: A rare bird, one of the 20 Ar 196A-1s delivered in 1939. Most went to 1/ and 5/ Bordfliegerstaffeln 196 for embarkation, but this one served with 10 (See)/LG2 at Travemünde.

Arado Ar 234 Blitz

Ar 234B-1 and B-2 Blitz

Origin: Arado Flugzeugwerke GmbH.
Type: Single-seat reconnaissance bomber.
Engines: Two 1,980lb (900kg) thrust Junkers Jumo 004B axial turbojets.
Dimensions: Span 46ft 3½in (14·2m); length 41ft 5½in (12·65m); height 14ft 1¼in (4·3m).
Weights: Empty 11,464lb (5200kg); loaded 18,541lb (8410kg); maximum with rocket takeoff boost 21,715lb (9850kg).
Performance: Maximum speed (clean) 461mph (742km/h); service ceiling 32,800ft (10,000m); range (clean) 1,013 miles (1630km), (with 3,300lb bomb load) 684 miles (1100km).
Armament: Two fixed MG 151 20mm cannon in rear fuselage, firing to rear and sighted by periscope; various combinations of bombs slung under fuselage and/or engines to maximum of 3,300lb (1500kg).
History: First flight (Ar 234V1) 15 June 1943, (Ar 234V9 with landing gear) March 1944, (Ar 234B-0 pre-production) 8 June 1944; operational delivery September 1944.
User: Germany (Luftwaffe).

Development: As the first jet reconnaissance bomber, the Ar 234 Blitz (meaning Lightning) spearheaded Germany's remarkably bold introduction of high-performance turbojet aircraft in 1944. Its design was begun under Walter Blume in 1941, after long studies in 1940 of an official specification for a jet-propelled reconnaissance aircraft with a range of 1,340 miles. The design was neat and simple, with two of the new axial engines slung under a high wing, and the single occupant in a pressurised cockpit forming the entire nose. But to achieve the required fuel capacity no wheels were fitted. When it flew on 15 June 1943 the first 234 took off from a three-wheel trolley and landed on retractable skids. After extensive trials with eight prototypes the ninth flew with conventional landing gear, leading through 20 pre-production models to the operational 234B-1, with ejection seat, autopilot and drop tanks under the engines. Main production centred on the 234B-2, made in many sub-variants, most of them able to carry a heavy bomb load. Service over the British Isles with the B-1 began in September 1944, followed by a growing force of B-2s which supported the Battle of the Bulge in the winter 1944–45. In March 1945 B-2s of III/KG76 repeatedly attacked the vital Remagen bridge across the Rhine with 2,205lb (1,000kg) bombs, causing its collapse. Though handicapped by fuel shortage these uninterceptable aircraft played a significant role on all European fronts in the closing months of the war, 210 being handed over excluding the many prototypes and later versions with four engines and an uncompleted example with a crescent-shaped wing.

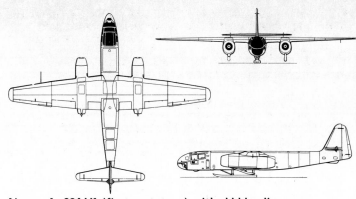

Above: Ar 234 V1 (first prototype) with skid landing gear.

Above: Take-off by the Ar 234 V9 (ninth prototype), first of the B-series with conventional landing gear. Other advanced features included pressure cabin, ejection seat and computer.

Blohm und Voss Bv 138

Bv 138A-1, B-1 and C-1 (data for C-1)

Origin: Hamburger Flugzeugbau GmbH.
Type: Six-crew reconnaissance flying boat.
Engines: Three 880hp Junkers Jumo 205D diesels with 12 opposed pistons in six cylinders.
Dimensions: Span 88ft 7in (27m); length 65ft 1½in (19·85m); height 19ft 4¼in (5·9m).
Weights: Empty 24,250lb (11,000kg); loaded 31,967lb (14,500kg); (rocket assist) 36,337lb (16,480kg).
Performance: Maximum speed 171mph (275km/h); climb to 10,000ft (3050m) in 24min; service ceiling 16,400ft (5000m); maximum range 2,500 miles (4023km).
Armament: 20mm MG 151 cannon in front and rear turrets; 13mm MG 131 in cockpit behind centre engine; four 331lb (150kg) depth charges or other stores under inner right wing.
History: First flight (Ha 138V-1) 15 July 1937; first delivery (A-1) January 1940; (C-1) 1941.
User: Germany (Luftwaffe).

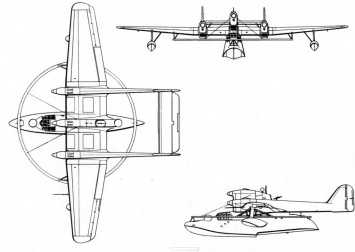

Above The Bv 138 MS minesweeper with degaussing ring.

Below: The definitive version was the Bv 138C, and examples served in many parts of Europe. This C-1 was operated by 3.(F)/SAGr 125, based at Constanza, Romania, on patrol over the Black Sea.

Right: Somewhere on the bitter Arctic convoy route this Bv 138C of SAGr 130 has made rendezvous with a U-boat—possibly to take on fuel oil for its diesels.

Below: The Ar 234 was the only jet bomber to be operational in World War II, and though it did not affect the course of the war its pinpricks were usually unstoppable. This B-2/P Blitz served with 9/KG 76 operating from Achmer in February 1945. It is seen with 1,102-lb (SC500) bombs hung under the nacelles, but the fuselage rack could carry a 3,086-pounder.

Below: In 1943 development began on a more powerful four-engined Ar 234C series. Some had twinned nacelles.

Development: Originally designated Ha 138, reflecting the fact that the aircraft subsidiary of the Blohm und Voss shipyard is (even today) Hamburger Flugzeugbau, the 138 was designed by Richard Vogt and took a long time to reach its final form. Major changes had to be made to the hull, wing, tail and tail booms, though none of the alterations were due to the unusual layout. The first 25 Bv 138A-1 boats were intended to be ocean reconnaissance platforms, but were not a success and ended up as transports in the Norwegian campaign and thereafter. They were underpowered with three 600hp Jumo 205 C diesel engines, the fuel oil being carried inside the tubular main spar of the wing. In late 1940 the Bv 138B-1 entered service with 880hp Jumo 205D engines, further modified tail and a 20mm turret at each end of the hull. After building 21, production was switched to the final Bv 138C-1, of which 227 were delivered in 1941–43. This had improved propellers, added a dorsal MG 131 and was greatly improved in equipment. Throughout 1942–45 the 138C gave good front-line service in the Arctic, the Baltic, the North Atlantic and Mediterranean.

Blohm und Voss Bv 222 Wiking

Bv 222 prototypes, 222A and 222C

Origin: Hamburger Flugzeugbau GmbH.
Type: Strategic transport flying boat (see text).
Engines: (Most) six 1,000hp Bramo (BMW) Fafnir 323R nine-cylinder radials, (V7 and 222C) six 980hp Junkers Jumo 207C six-cylinder (12-piston) diesels.
Dimensions: Span 150ft 11in (46·00m); length 121ft 4½in (37·00m); height 35ft 9in (10·9m).
Weights: Empty (A) about 64,000lb (29,000kg), (C) 67,572lb (30,650kg); maximum (all) 108,030lb (49,000kg).
Performance: Maximum speed (all) 242mph (390km/h) without armament, 183mph (295km/h) with; maximum cruise at height 214mph (345km/h), (armed) 156mph (252km/h); maximum range at 152mph (245km/h) 3,790 miles (6100km); endurance 28hr.
Armament: Varied greatly from single 7·92mm MG 81 to five/six power turrets; (C) 13mm MG 131 manually aimed in bow, 20mm MG 151 in one or two dorsal turrets and two wing turrets (upper surface behind outer nacelles) plus various MG 131 or MG 81 from side windows.
History: First flight 7 September 1940; first service mission 10 July 1941.
User: Germany (Luftwaffe).

Development: Deutsche Luft Hansa ordered three of the large Bv 222 boats in 1937 for use on the North and South Atlantic. The prototype (222V-1) was civil, but after initial flight trials was modified into a freight transport for the Luftwaffe. There followed nine further aircraft, no two alike, V9 also being the first of four production 222C-0 transports with Jumo engines and improved armament, as well as FuG 200 Hohentwiel radar and FuG 216 rear warning. Only 13 were flown, and decision to drop the diesels led to a switch to the Fafnir, used in the majority of the prototypes,

Right: The last of the radial-engined A-series was the V8, seen here on the slipway with all engines running. It served only a few weeks with LTS See 222 before being shot down.

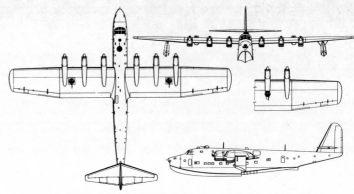

Above: Three-view of Bv 222C (V9); inset, right wing of V7.

from No 20, which with 14-19 were almost complete. From 1941 the Wikings shuttled from northern Norway to Africa bringing urgent stores. Despite their improving equipment, nearly all were shot down or destroyed at their moorings, but four survived to VE-day, one being scuttled by its crew and the others being flown to Britain and the USA for trials. The Wiking posed many development problems, and always seemed underpowered, but its basic qualities were good. From it derived the even bigger Bv 238, described at the end of the German section.

Dornier Do 17

Do 17E, F, K and P

Origin: Dornier-Werke GmbH.
Type: Three-seat medium bomber (17F, reconnaissance).
Engines: Two 750hp BMW VI 7·3 12-cylinder vee liquid-cooled; (17P) two 1,000hp BMW 132N nine-cylinder radials.
Dimensions: Span 59ft 0½in (18m); length (17E, F) 53ft 3¾in (16·25m); (17P) 52ft 9¾in (16·1m); height (17E, F) 14ft 2in (4·3m); (17P) 14ft 11in (4·57m).
Weights: Empty (17E, F) 9,921lb (4500kg); (17P) 10,140lb (4600kg); loaded (17E) 15,520lb (7050kg); (17F) 15,430lb (7000kg); (17P) 16,887lb (7660kg).
Performance: Maximum speed (17E, F) 220mph (355km/h); (17P) 249mph (400km/h); service ceiling (17E) 16,730ft (5100m); (17F) 19,685ft (6000m), (17P) 20,340ft (6200m); typical range (17E) 620 miles (1000km); (17F) 994 miles (1600km); (17P) 745 miles (1200km).
Armament: (17E) one 7·92mm MG 15 manually aimed from rear ventral hatch and one manually aimed to rear from dorsal position, with internal bomb load of 1,650lb (750kg); (17P) three MG 15s, one (normally fixed to fire ahead) in right windscreen, one in ventral hatch and one in dorsal position, with internal bomb load of 2,205lb (1000kg).
History: First flight (single-fin V1 prototype) autumn 1934; (Do 17E) 7 November 1936; (Do 17F) 10 November 1936; (Do 17P) late 1937.
Users: Germany (Luftwaffe), Jugoslavia, Soviet Union (2 aircraft only).

Development: Popularly dubbed "the flying pencil" in both Germany and Britain, the Do 17 was not planned as a bomber and secretly tested as a civil transport; its history was the other way round. Deutsche Luft Hansa decided its slender body left much too little room for the six passengers, but the Reichsluftfahrtministerium eventually decided the Do 17 was worth developing as a bomber. Numerous prototypes were built with different noses and engines and eventually the Do 17E-1 and the F-1 reconnaissance machine went into large-scale, and widely subcontracted, production for the embryo Luftwaffe. As early as March 1937 both were in combat service, with

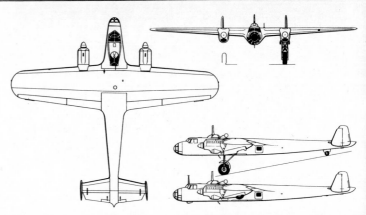

Above: Three-view of the first major Luftwaffe versions, the Do 17F-1 (reconnaissance) and (bottom) Do 17E-1 bomber.

one Staffel of 17Fs being in Spain with the Legion Kondor (there to prove virtually immune to interception by the Republican forces). In the spring of 1937 a Do 17M prototype with powerful DB 600 engines walked away from all the fighter aircraft at the International Military Aircraft Competition at Zurich. This caused a great sensation and the first nation to buy the new bomber was Jugoslavia, receiving 20 from Germany plus a construction licence. The Jugoslav Do 17Kb-1 had a very early nose profile (the same, in fact, as the Zurich demonstrator) and Gnome-Rhône 14N radial engines. They had a 20mm Hispano cannon and three 7·92mm Brownings. About 70 were on strength when the Germans invaded Jugoslavia in April 1941, two escaping to Greece with cargoes of gold bullion. The several hundred E and F models formed the biggest portion of the Luftwaffe bomber and reconnaissance force up to 1939, but by the end of that year had been relegated to operational training. The later Do 17M-1 (Bramo Fafnir radials of 1,000hp) and Do 17P succeeded the E and F in production during 1937 and saw combat during World War II. They were the final types to retain the slender "flying pencil" shape and hemispherical nose-cap.

Left: A BMW-radial-engined Do 17P-1 reconnaissance model, serving with 4.(F)/14 "Münchausen" Staffel. In 1939 this was with Luftflotte IV in Austria, Silesia and Czechoslovakia.

DFS 230

DFS 230A-1, B-1, C-1, F-1

Origin: Deutsches Forschungsinstitut für Segelflugzeug; production by Gothaer Waggonfabrik and others.
Type: Assault glider.
Dimensions: Span (nearly all) 68ft 5½in (20·87m); length (A, B, C) 36ft 10½in (11·24m); height 8ft 11¾in (2·74m).
Weights: Empty (B-1) 1,896lb (860kg); maximum (A-1) 4,608lb (2090 kg), (B-1) 4,630lb (2100kg).
Performance: Normal towing speed 130mph (210km/h); dive limit speed 180mph (290km/h).
History: First flight, early 1937; service delivery (A-0) 1938, (A-1) 1939.
User: Germany, and possibly other Axis countries.

Development: Apparently no serious thought had been given to the use of gliders in war until Ernst Udet, later head of the Luftwaffe technical procurement department, visited DFS in 1933. He later placed an order for a military transport glider, the DFS 230, which was flown with conspicuous success by Hanna Reitsch in 1937. After demonstrations before senior officers the DFS 230 became the basis around which the new technique of glider-borne assault was developed. On 10 May 1940 it was put into effect with total success by 45 gliders, towed by Ju 52s to carefully planned pinpoint operations on bridges and forts in the Low Countries. The classic assault was on Fort Eben Emael, in Belgium, on the Albert Canal. The vast modern fortress was knocked out and held by 72 men who arrived silently within the outer walls at dawn. They held until the German Army arrived more than 24hr later, suffering total casualties of six men killed and 20 wounded. In Crete large forces of DFS 230 and other gliders suffered heavily, but took the island. Hundreds of 230s were used in North Africa and Italy, with progressively less effect, but went out in a blaze of glory when Otto Skorzeny's handpicked force stormed the mountain-top hotel where Mussolini was being held under armed guard and flew him out in a Storch. Most 230s were of the B-1 type with braking parachute; the C-1 had three solid fuel rockets in the nose to stop it in 30 metres, and the F-1 was an enlarged model seating 15. Nearly all were delivered before 1941, output being 1,022.

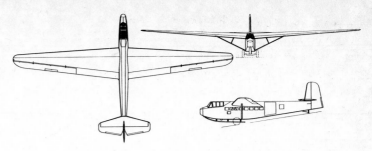

Above: Three-view of a typical DFS 230A-1 (wheels jettisoned).

Below: An operational DFS 230A-1 on tow, possibly during a combat mission. The tug was almost always the Ju 52/3m, and much research was done with close-coupled Starschlepp tows, used later in the war to tow heavy fuel tanks, bombs and even Fi 103 flying bombs.

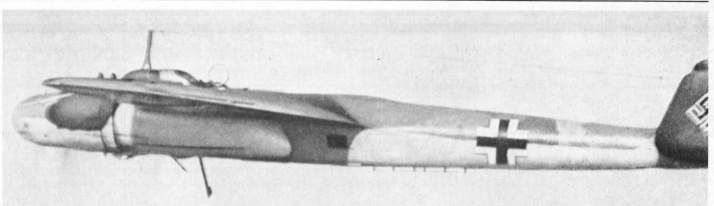

Above: In September 1939 the Do 17P-1 reconnaissance aircraft equipped 22 staffeln, but few were left a year later.

Below: Seen in the 1937 camouflage livery, this Do 17E-1 bomber had the benefit of combat experience in Spain.

Dornier Do 17Z and 215

Do 17Z-1 and -2 and Do 215A-1, B-1 and B-5

Origin: Dornier-Werke GmbH.
Type: Four-seat medium bomber and reconnaissance.
Engines: (Do 17Z-2) two 1,000hp Bramo Fafnir 323P nine-cylinder radials: (Do 215B-1) two 1,075hp Daimler-Benz DB 601A 12-cylinder inverted-vee liquid-cooled.
Dimensions: (Both) span 59ft 0½in (18m); length 51ft 9½in (15·79m); height 14ft 11½in (4·56m).
Weights: Empty (Do 17Z-2) 11,484lb (5210kg); (Do 215B-1) 12,730lb (5775kg); loaded (both) 19,841lb (9000kg).
Performance: Maximum speed (Do 17Z-2) 263mph (425km/h); (Do 215B-1) 280mph (450km/h); service ceiling (Do 17Z-2) 26,740ft (8150m); (Do 215B-1) 31,170ft (9500m); range with half bomb load (Do 17Z-2) 721 miles (1160km); (Do 215B-1) 932 miles (1500km).
Armament: Normally six 7·92mm Rheinmetall MG 15 machine guns, one fixed in nose, remainder on manually aimed mounts in front windscreen, two beam windows, and above and below at rear; internal bomb load up to 2205lb (1000kg).
History: First flight (Do 17S prototype) early 1938; (Do 17Z-2) early 1939; (Do 215V1 prototype) late 1938; first delivery (Do 17Z-1) January 1939, (Do 215A-1) December 1939; termination of production (Do 17Z series) July 1940, (Do 215 series) January 1941.
User: Germany (Luftwaffe).

Development: Whereas the slenderness of the first families of Do 17 bombers had earned them the nickname of "Flying Pencil", the Do 17S introduced a completely new front end with much deeper cabin and extensive window area all round. Such a change had been obvious from the inadequate defensive armament of the earlier models, revealed in the Spanish Civil War, and the penalty of increased weight and drag was to

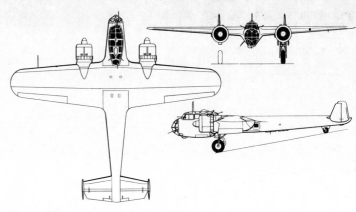

Above: Three-view of the Do 17Z-2.

some degree countered by a search for more powerful engines. The S prototype had DB 600 liquid-cooled engines, as did the Do 17U five-seat pathfinder, of which 12 were delivered to the nine Bomber Groups already using earlier Do 17s. The Do 17Z, powered by the Bramo radial engine, was at first underpowered and full bomb load had to await the more powerful Fafnir 323P of the 17Z-2. Between late 1939 and the summer of 1940 about 535 Do 17Z series bomber and reconnaissance machines were delivered and, though they suffered high attrition over Britain, they did much effective work and were the most popular and reliable of all Luftwaffe bombers of the early Blitzkrieg period. The Do 215 was the Do 17Z renumbered as an export version, with the more powerful DB 601 engine. The Do 215A-1 for Sweden became the Do 215B-0 and B-1 for the Luftwaffe and altogether 101 were put into service for bomber and reconnaissance roles; 12 were converted as Do 215B-5 night intruders, with a "solid" nose carrying two cannon and four machine guns, and operated by night over Britain before transfer to Sicily in October 1941.

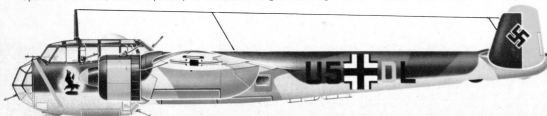

Left: The Z-2 bombers of III/KG 2 saw intense action in all campaigns up to 1941.

Below: Another Do 17Z-2 of KG 2 seen over the blue Aegean with an almost defenceless Greece ahead, in April 1941. Later, things got tougher.

Dornier Do 18

Do 18D, G, H, N

Origin: Dornier-Werke GmbH.
Type: D, G, reconnaissance and air/sea rescue; H, trainer, N, rescue.
Engines: (D) tandem push/pull Junkers Jumo 205C diesels, each rated at 600hp; (G, H, N) 700hp Jumo 205D.
Dimensions: Span 77ft 9in (23·7m); length 63ft 2in (19·25m); height 17ft 9in (5·45m).
Weights: (G-1) empty 12,900lb (5850kg); maximum 22,046lb (10,000 kg).
Performance: (G-1) Maximum speed at sea level 162mph (260km/h); typical cruise 106mph (170km/h); range 2,175 miles (3500km).
Armament: (D-1) typically one 7·92mm MG 15 manually aimed from bow and rear cockpits, with underwing racks for 1,102lb (500kg) load of weapons or stores on each side; (G-1) 13mm MG 131 in bow cockpit, 20mm MG 151 in power dorsal turret, same wing capacity; (H, N) none.
History: First flight (civil) 15 March 1935; (D) early 1938; final delivery, late 1939.
User: Germany (Luftwaffe, DLH).

Development: The Do 18, a pleasant and relatively harmless machine, was the first Luftwaffe type shot down by British aircraft in World War II; a flight of Skuas from *Ark Royal* caught three of the boats shadowing British warships on 26 September 1939 (and it is a fair reflection on the

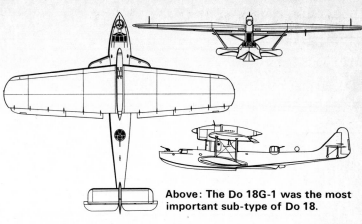

Above: The Do 18G-1 was the most important sub-type of Do 18.

Skua's capabilities as a fighter that two of the boats escaped). Only about 100 were delivered altogether, most being of the more powerful and better armed G version. Nearly all were confined to northern Europe and the Baltic/Atlantic areas. The N used to appear painted white, with prominent red crosses, though post-war evidence confirmed the belief that these sometimes were engaged in Elint (electronic intelligence) missions.

Below: One of the earlier variants was the Do 18D-1, one of which is seen on North Sea patrol (possibly with KüFlGr 106).

Dornier Do 24

Do 24T

Origin: Dornier-Werke GmbH; production by Weser, Aviolanda and Potez-CAMS (SNCAN); post-war, CASA, Spain.
Type: Reconnaissance flying boat (typical crew, six).
Engines: Three 1,000hp Bramo Fafnir 323R-2 nine-cylinder radials.
Dimensions: Span 88ft 7in (27m); length 72ft 2in (22m): height 17ft 10in (5·45m).
Weights: Empty 29,700lb (13,500kg); loaded 40,565lb (18,400kg).
Performance: Maximum speed 211mph (340km/h); service ceiling 19,360ft (5900m); maximum range 2,950 miles (4750km).
Armament: One 7·92mm MG 15 machine gun in bow turret, one MG 15 in tail turret and one 20mm MG 151/20 or 30mm MK 103 cannon in dorsal turret behind wing; underwing racks for 12 110lb (50kg) bombs or other stores.
History: First flight (Do 24V3) 3 July 1937; service delivery (Do 24K) November 1937; withdrawal from service (Spain) 1967.
Users: Germany, Netherlands, Spain, Sweden; post-war, France.

Below: The main Luftwaffe type was the Do 24T-1, this example being one of the 170 supplied from the Netherlands in 1941-44.

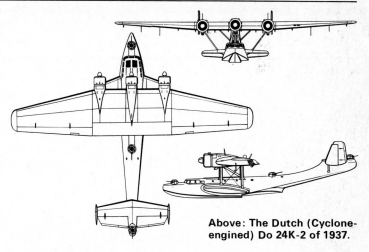

Above: The Dutch (Cyclone-engined) Do 24K-2 of 1937.

Development: This excellent trimotor flying boat was one of the very few aircraft of the Nazi period to be designed for a foreign government. The customer was the Netherlands and by 1940 a total of 11 had been built by Weserflugzeugbau and flown out to the Dutch East Indies naval air service (MLD). In addition, 26 more had been supplied by the Dutch de Schelde and Aviolanda companies, under a government-purchased licence. After the invasion of the Low Countries production was continued in Holland for the Luftwaffe, with the French Potez-CAMS factory at Sartrouville also assigned to Do 24 production in 1941. Production for the Luftwaffe amounted to 170 in Holland and 48 in France and the type was met all round the European coasts. One force-landed in Sweden in 1944, was impressed into RSAF service as the Tp 24 and not surrendered to the USSR until 1951. After VE-day the CAMS factory continued in production, making a further 20 aircraft to augment ex-Luftwaffe machines for a force of more than 60 in Aéronavale service until 1955. The remaining aircraft were sold to Spain to augment an original force of 12 purchased from Germany in 1944. Designated HR-5, the Do 24T-3 in Spain and the Spanish Mediterranean and Atlantic islands was the last type of large military flying boat operating in Europe. Since 1969 Dornier has been seeking markets for the proposed Do 24/72 development, powered by three 1,800hp Lycoming turboprops.

Dornier Do 217

Do 217E-2, K-2, M-1, J-2/N-2, P-1

Origin: Dornier-Werke GmbH.

Type: (E, K, M) four-seat bomber; (J, N) three-seat night fighter; (P) four-seat high-altitude reconnaissance.

Engines: (E-2, J-2) two 1,580hp BMW 801A or 801M 18-cylinder two-row radials; (K-2) two 1,700hp BMW 801D; (M-1, N-2) two 1,750hp Daimler-Benz DB 603A 12-cylinder inverted-vee liquid-cooled; (P-1) two 1,860hp DB 603B supercharged by DB 605T in the fuselage.

Dimensions: Span 62ft 4in (19m); (K-2) 81ft 4½in (24·8m); (P-1) 80ft 4in (24·4m); length 56ft 9¼in (17·3m); (E-2 with early dive brakes) 60ft 10½in (18·5m); (K-2 and M-1) 55ft 9in (17m); (J and N) 58ft 9in (17·9); (P) 58ft 11in (17·95m); height 16ft 5in (5m) (all versions same within 2in).

Weights: Empty (E-2) 19,522lb (8850kg); (M-1) 19,985 (9000kg); (K-2, J and N) all about 21,000lb (9450kg); (P) about 23,000lb (10,350kg); loaded (E-2) 33,070lb (15,000kg); (K-2, M-1) 36,817lb (16,570kg); (J and N) 30,203lb (13,590kg); (P) 35,200lb (15,840kg).

Performance: Maximum speed (E-2) 320mph (515km/h); (K-2) 333mph (533km/h); (M-1) 348mph (557km/h); (J and N) about 311mph (498km/h); (P) 488mph (781km/h); service ceiling (E-2) 24,610ft (7500m); (K-2) 29,530ft (9000m); (M-1) 24,140ft (7358m); (J and N) 27,560ft (8400m); (P) 53,000ft (16,154m); range with full bomb load, about 1,300 miles (2100km) for all versions.

Armament: (E-2) one fixed 15mm MG 151/15 in nose, one 13mm MG 131 in dorsal turret, one MG 131 manually aimed at lower rear, and three 7·92mm MG 15 manually aimed in nose and beam windows; maximum bomb load 8818lb (4000kg), including 3307lb (1500kg) external; (K-2)

Dornier Do 217K-1 cutaway drawing key:
1 Starboard rudder tab
2 Rudder controls
3 Rudder mass balance (lead insert)
4 Starboard tailfin
5 Leading-edge slot
6 Tailplane/tailfin attachment
7 Elevator
8 Elevator mass balance
9 Fixed tab
10 Trim tab
11 Tailplane construction
12 Elevator controls
13 Rear navigation light
14 Four aft-firing 7·9-mm MG 81 machine guns (*Rüstsatz* [field conversion set] 19)
15 Ammunition boxes
16 Tailplane trim control
17 Fuel emergency jettison
18 Mudguard
19 Tailwheel
20 Tailwheel doors
21 Tailwheel retraction mechanism
22 Tailplane carry-through
23 Fuselage skinning
24 Master compass
25 Dipole antenna
26 Anti-collision beacon
27 Elevator mass balance
28 Port tailfin
29 Leading-edge slot
30 Bomb bay division
31 Bomb bay hinge line
32 Bomb bay rear bulkhead entry/inspection hatch
33 Spherical oxygen cylinders
34 Starboard mainwheel
35 Mudguard
36 Mainwheel doors
37 Mainwheel retraction mechanism
38 Mainwheel well
39 FuG 25 (A-A recognition)
40 FuG 101 radio altimeter
41 Outer section split flaps
42 Starboard aileron
43 Aileron tab
44 Control lines
45 Rear spar
46 Braced wing ribs
47 Intermediate ribs
48 EGS 101 antenna
49 Starboard navigation light
50 Front spar
51 Leading-edge hot-air de-icing
52 Hot-air duct
53 Balloon-cable cutter in leading-edge
54 Starboard outer fuel tank (35 lmp gal/160l capacity)
55 Starboard oil tank (51·7 lmp gal/235l capacity)
56 Flame-damping exhaust pipes
57 Sliding-ring cooling air exit
58 BMW 801D 14-cylinder two-row radial engine
59 Annular oil cooler
60 VDM Three-blade metal propeller of 12·79ft (3·90m) diameter
61 Cooling fan
62 Cowling sliding nose-ring
63 Propeller boss
64 Starboard inner fuel tank (175 lmp gal/795l capacity)
65 Fuselage main fuel tank (231 lmp gal/1050l capacity)
66 Wing spar carry-through
67 Bomb bay top hinge line
68 Load-bearing beam
69 Bomb shackle
70 Bomb bay centre hinge line
71 Typical bomb load: two 2,205-lb (1000-kg) SC 1000 bombs
72 Forward bomb doors
73 13-mm MG 131 machine gun in ventral position (1,000 rounds)

74 Ammunition ejection chute
75 Ventral gunner's station
76 Armoured bulkhead
77 Cartridge collector box
78 Batteries (two 24-Volt)
79 Radio equipment
80 Dorsal gunner's seat support
81 Cabin hot-air
82 Dorsal gunner's station
83 Armoured turret ring
84 Aerial mast
85 Gun safety guard
86 Starboard beam-mounted 7·9-mm MG 81 machine gun (750 rounds)
87 13-mm MG 131 machine gun (500 rounds)
88 Electrically-operated dorsal turret
89 Revi gunsight
90 Angled side windows
91 Jettisonable decking
92 Bomb-aimer's folding seat
93 Navigator's table
94 Pilot's contoured seat
95 Rear-view gunsight
96 Upper instrument panel
97 Nose glazing
98 Control horns
99 Engine controls
100 One 13-mm MG 131 in strengthened nose glazing (alternatively twin 7·9-mm MG 81Z)
101 Balloon-cable cutter in nose horizontal frame

102 Cartridge ejection chute
103 Ammunition feed
104 Lotfe 7D bombsight
105 Bomb aimer's flat panel
106 Control column counterweight
107 Nose armour
108 Ventral gunner's quilt
109 Ammunition box (nose MG 131)
110 Cartridge collector box
111 Entry hatch
112 Entry hatch (open)
113 Entry ladder
114 Port mainwheel doors
115 Mudguard
116 Port mainwheel
117 Mainwheel leg cross struts
118 Port engine cowling
119 Landing light (swivelling)
120 Control linkage
121 Pitot head
122 Port navigation light
123 Port aileron
124 Aileron trim tab

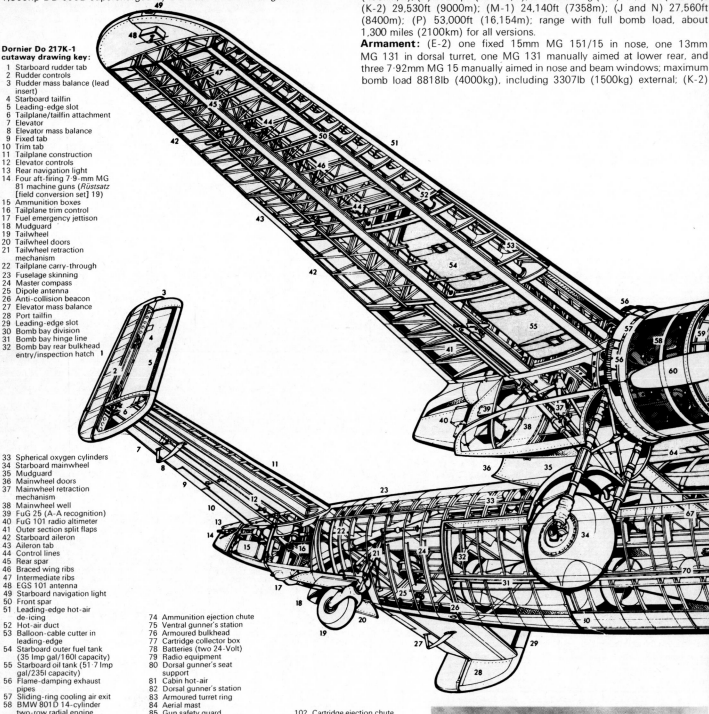

Above: The sixth pre-production Do 217E-0 was used by BMW for engine development.

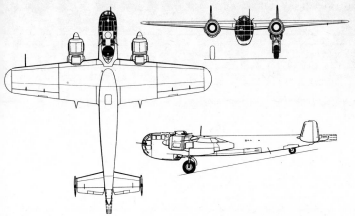

Above: The Do 217K-1 with new cockpit but original wing.

defensive armament similar to E-2, plus battery of four 7·92mm MG 81 fixed rearward-firing in tail and optional pair fixed rearward-firing in nacelles (all sighted and fired by pilot), and offensive load of two FX 1400 radio-controlled glide bombs and/or (K-3 version) two Hs 293 air-to-surface rocket guided missiles; (M-1) as E-2 except MG 15s replaced by larger number of MG 81; (J-2 and N-2) typically four 20mm MG FF cannon and four 7·92mm MG 17 in nose plus MG 131 for lower rear defence (N-2 often had later guns such as MG 151/20 in nose and MG 151/20 or MK 108 30mm in Schräge Musik upward-firing installation); (P) three pairs of MG 81 for defence, and two 1102lb bombs on underwing racks.

History: First flight (Do 217V1) August 1938; (pre-production Do 217A-0) October or November 1939; first delivery of E series, late 1940; termination of production, late 1943.

Users: Germany (Luftwaffe), (217 J) Italy (RA).

Development: Superficially a scaled-up Do 215, powered at first by the same DB 601 engines, the 217 was actually considerably larger and totally

▶

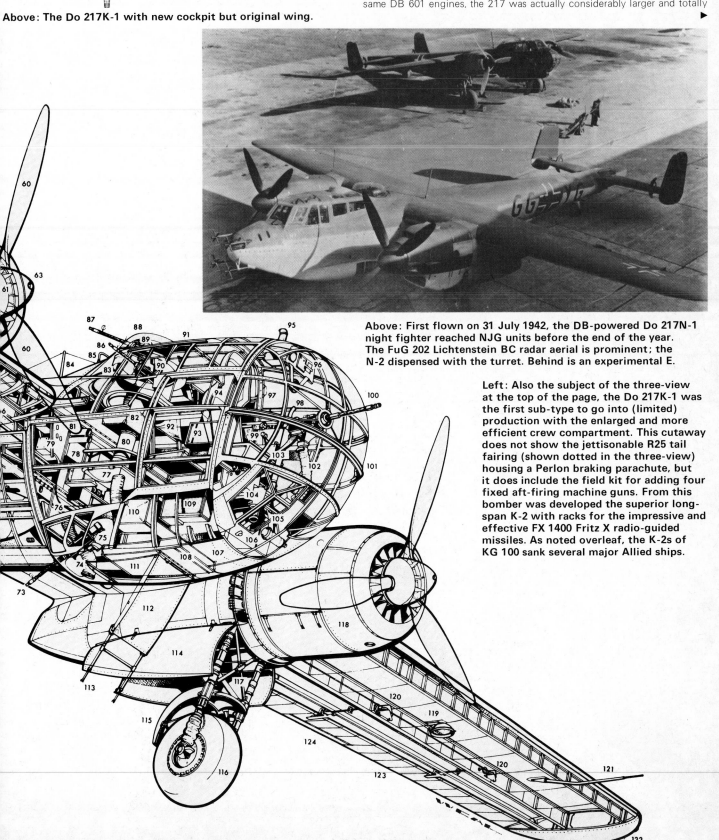

Above: First flown on 31 July 1942, the DB-powered Do 217N-1 night fighter reached NJG units before the end of the year. The FuG 202 Lichtenstein BC radar aerial is prominent; the N-2 dispensed with the turret. Behind is an experimental E.

Left: Also the subject of the three-view at the top of the page, the Do 217K-1 was the first sub-type to go into (limited) production with the enlarged and more efficient crew compartment. This cutaway does not show the jettisonable R25 tail fairing (shown dotted in the three-view) housing a Perlon braking parachute, but it does include the field kit for adding four fixed aft-firing machine guns. From this bomber was developed the superior long-span K-2 with racks for the impressive and effective FX 1400 Fritz X radio-guided missiles. As noted overleaf, the K-2s of KG 100 sank several major Allied ships.

different in detail design. Much of Dornier's efforts in 1938–40 were devoted to finding more powerful engines and improving the flying qualities, and when the BMW 801 radial was available the 217 really got into its stride and carried a heavier bomb load than any other Luftwaffe bomber of the time. Early E models, used from late 1940, had no dorsal turret and featured a very long extension of the rear fuselage which opened into an unusual dive brake. This was soon abandoned, but the 217 blossomed out into a prolific family which soon included the 217J night fighter, often produced by converting E-type bombers, and the N which was likewise produced by converting the liquid-cooled M. Several series carried large air-to-surface missiles steered by radio command from a special crew station in the bomber. Long-span K-2s of III/KG 100 scored many successes with their

formidable missiles in the Mediterranean, their biggest bag being the Italian capital ship *Roma* as she steamed to the Allies after Italy's capitulation. The pressurised high-altitude P series had fantastic performance that would have put them out of reach of any Allied fighters had they been put into service in time. From 1943, Dornier devoted more effort to the technically difficult Do 317, which never went into service.

Below: This Do 217, Werk-Nr 4572, was the first of the K-2 family. Major structural stiffening allowed the span to be increased to about 81ft 4½in, enabling the aircraft to lift additional fuel and two of the Fritz X guided missiles which weighed 3,454lb each.

Dornier Do 335 Pfeil

Do 335A-1 and A-6

Origin: Dornier-Werke GmbH.
Type: (A-1) single-seat fighter, (A-6) two-seat night fighter.
Engines: Two 1,900hp Daimler-Benz DB 603G 12-cylinder inverted-vee liquid-cooled, in push/pull arrangement.
Dimensions: Span 45ft 4in (13·8m); length 45ft 6in (13·87m); height 16ft 4in (4m).
Weights: Empty (A-1) 16,314lb (7400kg); (A-6) 16,975lb (7700kg); maximum loaded (both) 25,800lb (11,700kg).
Performance: Maximum speed (A-1) 413mph (665km/h) sustained; 477mph (765km/h) emergency boost (A-6 about 40mph slower in each case); initial climb (A-1) 4,600ft (1400m)/min; service ceiling (A-1) 37,400ft (11,410m); (A-6) 33,400ft (10,190m); maximum range (both) 1,280 miles (2050km) clean, up to 2,330 miles (3750km) with drop tank.
Armament: Typical A-1, one 30mm MK 103 cannon firing through front propeller hub and two 15mm MG 151/15 above nose; underwing racks for light stores and centreline rack for 1,100lb (500kg) bomb; A-6 did not carry bomb and usually had 15mm guns replaced by 20mm MG 151/20s.
History: First flight (Do 335V1) autumn 1943; (production A-1) late November 1944.
User: Germany (Luftwaffe).

Development: Dornier took out a patent in 1937 for an aircraft powered by two engines, one behind the other, in the fuselage, driving tractor and pusher propellers. In 1939–40 Schempp-Hirth built the Gö 9 research aircraft to test the concept of a rear propeller driven by an extension shaft and in 1941 work began on the Do 231 fighter-bomber. This was replaced by the Do 335 and by first flight Dornier had orders for 14 prototypes, ten preproduction A-0s, 11 production A-1s and three dual-control trainer A-10 and A-12 with stepped tandem cockpits. At high speed the 335 was prone to unpleasant porpoising and snaking, but production continued on the A-1, the A-4 reconnaissance batch and the A-6 with FuG 220 radar operated by a rear-seat observer. Though heavy, the 335 was strong and very fast and was notable in having the first production type of ejection seat (for obvious reasons). By VE-day about 90 aircraft had been rolled out, more than 60 flown and about 20 delivered to combat units. Work was also well advanced on a number of versions of the Do 335B heavy fighter, with added 30mm MK 108 cannon in the wings (some having two-stage engines and long-span wings), the Do 435 with various very powerful engines, and the twinned Do 635 with two Do 335 fuselages linked by a new parallel centre-section. The 635, which was being designed and produced by Junkers as the 8-635, would have weighed 72,000lb as a reconnaissance aircraft, and flown 4,050 miles cruising at 398mph. Pfeil means "arrow".

Right: The only Pfeil in existence is this completely rebuilt exhibit. It was originally the second Do 335A-0, flying in late May 1944. In 1945 it was taken to the USA, languished at the Smithsonian's Silver Hill store, and 25 years later was returned to Germany and restored by Dornier at Oberpfaffenhofen.

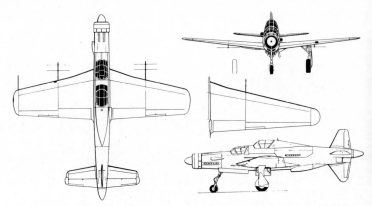

Above: Three-view of the Do 335A-6 two-seat night fighter with (inset) the long-span wing of B-8.

Below: The Do 335 V9, completed to full production standard and tested at Rechlin in May 1944.

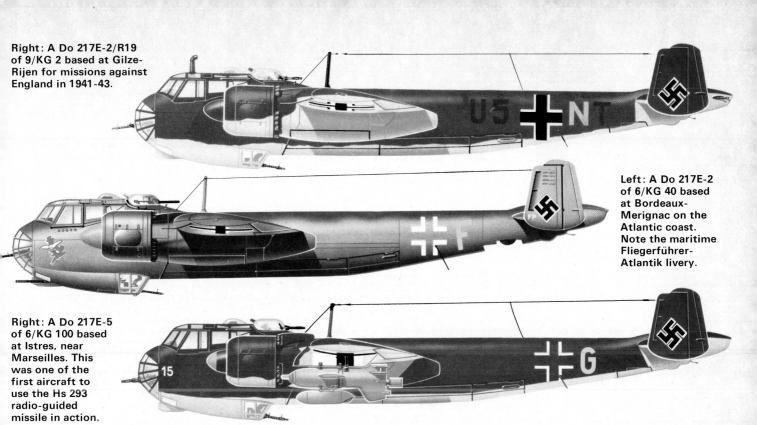

Right: A Do 217E-2/R19 of 9/KG 2 based at Gilze-Rijen for missions against England in 1941-43.

Left: A Do 217E-2 of 6/KG 40 based at Bordeaux-Merignac on the Atlantic coast. Note the maritime Fliegerführer-Atlantik livery.

Right: A Do 217E-5 of 6/KG 100 based at Istres, near Marseilles. This was one of the first aircraft to use the Hs 293 radio-guided missile in action.

Above: An earlier picture of the second A-0, the same machine as seen on the opposite page. It was used by EKdo 335.

Below: The Do 335 V3, like the second prototype, differed in many respects from the V1 flown in October 1943.

Fieseler Fi 156 Storch

Fi 156A, C, D, E, Fi 256

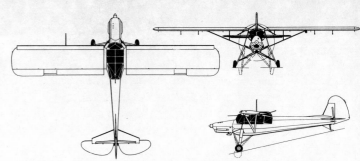

Above: Fi 156C-1, with in-flight landing-gear position dotted.

Origin: Gerhard Fieseler Werke GmbH, Kassel; production almost entirely by Morane-Saulnier, Puteaux, and Benes-Mraz, Czechoslovakia.
Type: STOL multi-role, see text.
Engine: (Almost all) 240hp Argus As 10C inverted-vee-8 aircooled; certain sub-types used other As 10 models of 260 or 270hp.
Dimensions: Span 46ft 9in (14·25m); length 32ft 5¾in (9·90m); height 9ft 10in (3·00m).
Weights: (Typical C) empty 2,050lb (930kg); maximum 2,910lb (1320kg).
Performance: Maximum speed 109mph (175km/h); minimum speed 32mph (51km/h); ground run (takeoff) 213ft (65m), (landing) 61ft (20m); range (max payload) 236 miles (380km), (max fuel) 600 miles (966km) at 60mph (97km/h).
History: First flight May 1936; service delivery, about May 1937; final delivery (France) 1949.
Users: Bulgaria, Croatia, Finland, France (1944 onwards), Germany, Hungary, Italy, Romania, Slovakia, Switzerland; captured specimens by most Allied air forces.

Development: Though only about 2,700 Storch (Stork) were built for the Axis, 2,549 of them during the war, it was used on every European front and for a vast range of duties. It beat two aeroplanes and a helicopter in a 1935 RLM competition for a STOL army co-op, casevac and liaison

Focke-Wulf Fw 44

Fw 44A, B and C Stieglitz (Goldfinch)

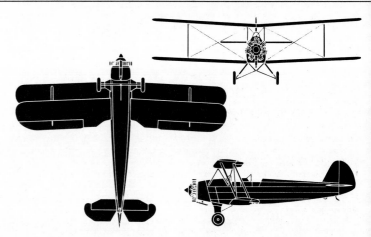

Above: Three-view of typical Fw 44C with wheeled landing gear.

Origin: Focke-Wulf Flugzeugbau, Bremen; licence-built in Argentina, Austria, Brazil, Bulgaria and Sweden.
Type: Primary trainer (also civil sporting aircraft).
Engine: (Fw 44A and C) 150hp Siemens Sh 14A seven-cylinder radial.
Dimensions: Span 29ft 6¼in (9·00m); length 23ft 11½in (7·30m); height 8ft 10¼in (2·70m).
Weights: Fw 44C empty 1,158lb (525kg); loaded (aerobatic) 1,698lb (770kg), (normal) 1,918lb (870kg).
Performance: Maximum speed 115mph (185km/h); range 419 miles (675km).
History: First flight September 1932; final delivery after 1938.
Users: Argentina, Austria, Bolivia, Brazil, Bulgaria, Chile, China, Colombia, Czechoslovakia, Finland, Germany (Luftwaffe and Luftdienst), Hungary, Romania, Sweden and Turkey.

Development: Designed under Kurt Tank in 1931 as the A44 (from the former Albatross-werke), the Fw 44 was the first really big success by Focke-Wulf and many thousands were made over a period of about a decade. At least 300 were exported prior to World War II, some of these being of the Fw 44B type with 120hp Argus As 8 inverted four-in-line engine. Of mixed construction, this trim tandem-seat biplane was delightful to fly and fully aerobatic. The cockpits had small fold-down side doors, bucket seats for a seat-type parachute and a folding rear seat for access to a baggage locker where a blind-flying hood could be clipped. In winter many Luftwaffe Stieglitz operated on skis. This popular machine equipped

at least ten of the regular Flugzeugführerschulen (FFS, pilot schools) and the officer candidate school at Fürstenfeldbruck, Munich.

Below: The Fw 44 was one of the mass-produced aircraft of the Luftwaffe, but unlike the Ar 66 and Go 145 it was not used as a tactical attacker by night. A curious feature of nearly all Focke-Wulfe aircraft of 1930-38 was the tail, with high tailplane ahead of the fin (and often with small auxiliary fins).

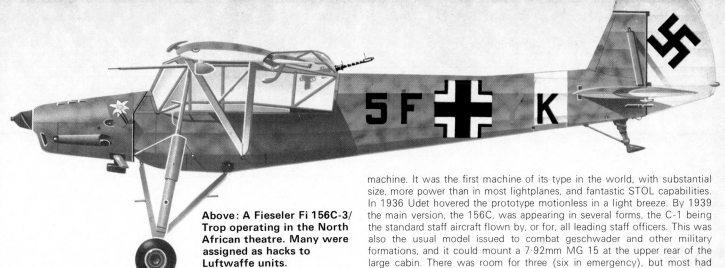

Above: A Fieseler Fi 156C-3/
Trop operating in the North
African theatre. Many were
assigned as hacks to
Luftwaffe units.

Left: One of the first production Fi 156C-1 Storch STOL
aircraft making a tail-high full-flap landing (note full up-
elevator). The Storch was large enough to fly many kinds of
battlefield mission, and its only significant shortcoming was
slow cruising speed (never more than 93mph). Feldmarschall
Kesselring eventually switched to the faster Fw 189.

machine. It was the first machine of its type in the world, with substantial
size, more power than in most lightplanes, and fantastic STOL capabilities.
In 1936 Udet hovered the prototype motionless in a light breeze. By 1939
the main version, the 156C, was appearing in several forms, the C-1 being
the standard staff aircraft flown by, or for, all leading staff officers. This was
also the usual model issued to combat geschwader and other military
formations, and it could mount a 7·92mm MG 15 at the upper rear of the
large cabin. There was room for three (six in emergency), but most had
only two seats. The side windows were wider than the rest of the fuselage,
so that a small lower row could give vertical downwards vision. Another
important series were the D sub-types with large side doors for a stretcher.
Morane-Saulnier developed the wide five-seat Fi 256, but flew only two
before the Germans departed. In 1944 Morane continued production, the
post-war MS.500 Criquet having a Salmson radial. Mraz likewise kept
building a version called K-65 Cap.

Focke-Wulf Fw 189 Uhu

Fw 189A-1, -2 and -3

Origin: Focke-Wulf Flugzeugbau GmbH; built under Focke-Wulf control
by SNCASO, with outer wings from Breguet.
Type: Three-seat reconnaissance and close support.
Engines: Two 465hp Argus As 410A-1 12 cylinder inverted-vee air-
cooled.
Dimensions: Span 60ft 4½in (18·4m); length 39ft 4½in (12m); height
10ft 2in (3·1m).
Weights: Empty 5,930lb (2690kg); loaded 8,708lb (3950kg).
Performance: Maximum speed 217mph (350km/h); climb to 13,120ft
(4000m) in 8 min 20sec; service ceiling 23,950ft (7300m); range 416 miles
(670km).
Armament: (A-2) one 7·92mm MG17 machine gun in each wing root,
twin 7·92mm MG81 manually aimed in dorsal position and (usually) twin
MG 81 in rear cone with limited field of fire; underwing racks for four
110lb (50kg) bombs.
History: First flight (Fw 189V1) July 1938; first delivery (pre-production
Fw 189A-0) September 1940; final delivery August 1944.
User: Germany (Luftwaffe), Hungary, Slovakia.

Development: Today the diversity of aircraft layout makes us forget how
odd this aircraft seemed. It looked strange to the customer also, but after
outstandingly successful flight trials the 189 Uhu (Owl) was grudgingly
bought in quantity as a standard reconnaissance aircraft. Though it flew in
numbers well before the war — no two prototypes being alike — it was
unknown by the Allies until it was disclosed in 1941 as "the Flying Eye" of
the German armies. On the Eastern front it performed beyond all expectation,
for it retained its superb handling (which made it far from a sitting duck to
fighters) and also showed great toughness of structure and more than once
returned to base with one tail shot off or removed by Soviet ramming attack.
Attempts to produce special attack versions with small heavily armoured
nacelles were not so successful, but 10 Fw 189B trainers were built with a
conventional nacelle having side-by-side dual controls in a normal cockpit,
with an observer above the trailing edge. The Fw 189A-3 was another dual-
control version having the normal "glasshouse". Eventually the sole source
became French factories with assembly at Bordeaux-Mérignac (today the
Dassault Mirage plant), which halted as Allied armies approached. There
were many different versions and several developments with more powerful
engines, but the basic A-1, A-2 (better armament) and A-3 were the only
types built in numbers, the total of these versions being 846.

**Right: Close tactical work by a Uhu on the Eastern Front; the
soldier is a member of a Luftwaffe ground reconnaissance unit.**

**Below: An Fw 189A-1 of 1.(H)/32 at Petsamo in northern
Finland in December 1942. Aircooled engines never froze.**

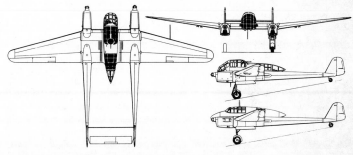

Above: Fw 189A-2 with additional side view (lower) of B-0.

Focke-Wulf Fw 190 and Ta 152

Fw 190A series, D series, F series, G series and Ta 152

Origin: Focke-Wulf Flugzeugbau GmbH; extremely dispersed manufacture and assembly, and part-subcontracted to Brandt (SNCA du Centre), France; also built in France post-war.
Type: Single-seat fighter bomber.
Engine: (A-8, F-8) one 1,700hp (2,100hp emergency boost) BMW 801Dg 18-cylinder two-row radial; (D-9) one 1,776hp (2,240hp emergency boost) Junkers Jumo 213A-1 12-cylinder inverted-vee liquid-cooled; (Ta 152H-1) one 1,880hp (2,250hp) Jumo 213E-1.
Dimensions: Span 34ft 5½in (10.49m); (Ta 152H-1) 47ft 6¾in (14.5m); length (A-8, F-8) 29ft 0in (8.84m); (D-9) 33ft 5¼in (10.2m); (Ta 152H-1) 35ft 5½in (10.8m); height 13ft 0in (3.96m); (D-9) 11ft 0¼in (3.35m); (Ta 152H-1) 11ft 8in (3.55m).

Above: A pair of Fw 190G-3 extended-range fighter-bombers flying over Romania, possibly in service with II/SG 10, in early 1944. By this time the Fw 190 was the most important Luftwaffe multi-role tactical aircraft on all fronts.

Focke-Wulf Fw 190A-8 cutaway drawing key:

1 Pitot head
2 Starboard navigation light
3 Detachable wingtip
4 Pitot tube heater cable
5 Wing lower shell 'floating rib'
6 Aileron hinge
7 Wing lower shell stringers
8 Leading-edge ribs
9 Front spar
10 Outboard 'solid rib'
11 Wing upper shell stringers
12 Aileron trim tab
13 Aileron structure
14 Aileron control linkage
15 Ammunition box (125 rounds)
16 Starboard 20mm Mauser MG 151/20E cannon (sideways mounted)
17 Ammunition box rear suspension arm
18 Flap structure
19 Wing flap upper skinning
20 Flap setting indicator peep-hole
21 Rear spar
22 Inboard wing construction
23 Undercarriage indicator
24 Wing rib strengthening
25 Ammunition feed chute
26 Static and dynamic air pressure lines
27 Cannon barrel
28 Launch tube bracing struts
29 Launch tube carrier strut
30 Mortar launch tube (auxiliary underwing armament)
31 Launch tube internal guide rails
32 21cm (WfrGr.21) spin-stabilized Type 42 mortar shell
33 VDM three-blade constant-speed propeller
34 Propeller boss
35 Propeller hub
36 Starboard undercarriage fairing
37 Starboard mainwheel
38 Oil warming chamber
39 Thermostat
40 Cooler armoured ring (6.5mm)
41 Oil tank drain valve
42 Annular oil tank (12.1 gal/55 litres)
43 Oil cooler
44 Twelve-blade engine cooling fan; 3.17 times propeller speed
45 Hydraulic-electric pitch control unit
46 Primer fuel line
47 Bosch magneto
48 Oil tank armour (5.5mm)
49 Supercharger air pressure pipes
50 BMW 801D-2 fourteen-cylinder radial engine
51 Cowling support ring
52 Cowling quick-release fasteners
53 Oil pump
54 Fuel pump (engine rear face)
55 Oil filter (starboard)
56 Wing root cannon synchronization gear
57 Gun troughs/cowling upper panel attachment
58 Engine mounting ring

59 Cockpit heating pipe
60 Exhaust pipes (cylinders 11–14)
61 MG 131 link and case chute
62 Engine bearer assembly
63 MG 131 ammunition boxes (400 rpg)
64 Fuel filter recess housing
65 MG 131 ammunition cooling pipes
66 MG 131 synchronization gear
67 Ammunition feed chute
68 Twin fuselage 13mm Rheinmetall MG 131 guns
69 Windscreen mounting frame
70 Emergency power fuse and distributor box
71 Rear-hinged gun access panel
72 Engine bearer/bulkhead attachment
73 Control column
74 Transformer
75 Aileron control torsion bar
76 Rubber pedals (EC pedal unit with hydraulic wheel-brake operation)
77 Fuselage/wing spar attachment
78 Adjustable rudder push rod
79 Fuel filler head
80 Cockpit floor support frame
81 Throttle lever
82 Pilot's seat back plate armour (8mm)
83 Seat guide rails
84 Side-section back armour (5mm)
85 Shoulder armour (5mm)
86 Oxygen supply valve
87 Steel frame turnover pylon
88 Windscreen spray pipes
89 Instrument panel shroud
90 30mm armoured glass quarterlights
91 50mm armoured glass windscreen
92 Revi 16B reflector gunsight
93 Canopy
94 Aerial attachment
95 Headrest
96 Head armour (12mm)
97 Head armour support strut
98 Explosive-charge canopy emergency jettison unit
99 Canopy channel slide
100 Auxiliary tank: fuel (25.3 gal/115 litres) or GM-1 (18.7 gal/85 litres)
101 FuG 16ZY radio transmitter-receiver
102 Handhold cover
103 Primer fuel filler cap
104 Autopilot steering unit (PKS 12)
105 FuG 16ZY power transformer
106 Entry step cover plate
107 Two tri-spherical oxygen bottles (starboard fuselage wall)
108 Auxiliary fuel tank filler point
109 FuG 25a transponder unit
110 Autopilot position integration unit
111 FuG 16ZY homer bearing converter
112 Elevator control cables
113 Rudder control DUZ-flexible rods
114 Fabric panel (Bulkhead 12)

115 Rudder differential unit
116 Aerial lead-in
117 Rear fuselage lift tube
118 Triangular stress frame
119 Tailplane trim unit
120 Tailplane attachment fitting
121 Tailwheel retraction guide tube
122 Retraction cable lower pulley
123 Starboard tailplane
124 Aerial
125 Starboard elevator
126 Elevator trim tab
127 Tailwheel shock strut guide
128 Fin construction
129 Retraction cable upper pulley
130 Aerial attachment stub
131 Rudder upper hinge
132 Rudder structure

133 Rudder trim tab
134 Tailwheel retraction mechanism access panel
135 Rudder attachment/actuation fittings
136 Rear navigation light
137 Extension spring
138 Elevator trim tab
139 Port elevator structure
140 Tailplane construction
141 Semi-retracting tailwheel
142 Forked wheel housing
143 Drag yoke
144 Tailwheel shock strut
145 Tailwheel locking linkage
146 Elevator actuation lever linkage
147 Angled frame spar
148 Elevator differential bellcrank
149 FuG 25a ventral aerial
150 Master compass sensing unit
151 FuG 16ZY fixed loop homing aerial
152 Radio compartment access hatch
153 Single tri-spherical oxygen bottle (port fuselage wall)
154 Retractable entry step
155 Wing-root fairing
156 Fuselage rear fuel tank (64.5 gal/293 litres)
157 Fuselage/rear spar attachment
158 Fuselage forward fuel tank (51 gal/232 litres)
159 Port wing root cannon ammunition box (250 rounds)
160 Ammunition feed chute
161 Wing root MG 151/20E cannon
162 Link and case chute
163 Cannon rear mount support bracket
164 Upper and lower wing shell stringers
165 Rear spar
166 Spar construction
167 Flap position indicator scale and peep-hole

168 Flap actuating electric motor
169 MG 151/20E cannon (sideways mounted)
170 Aileron transverse linkage
171 Ammunition box (125 rounds)
172 Ammunition box rear suspension arm
173 Aileron control linkage
174 Aileron control unit
175 Aileron trim tab

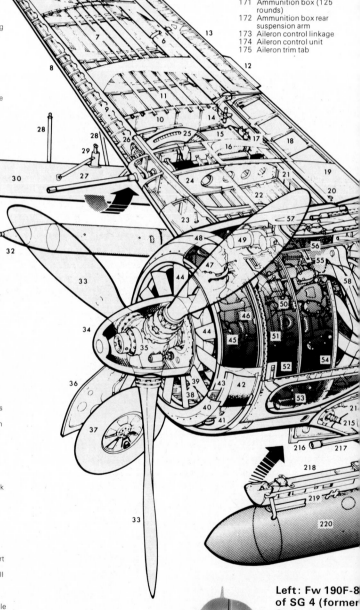

Left: Fw 190F-8 of SG 4 (former Stuka unit) at Köln-Wahn, December 1944.

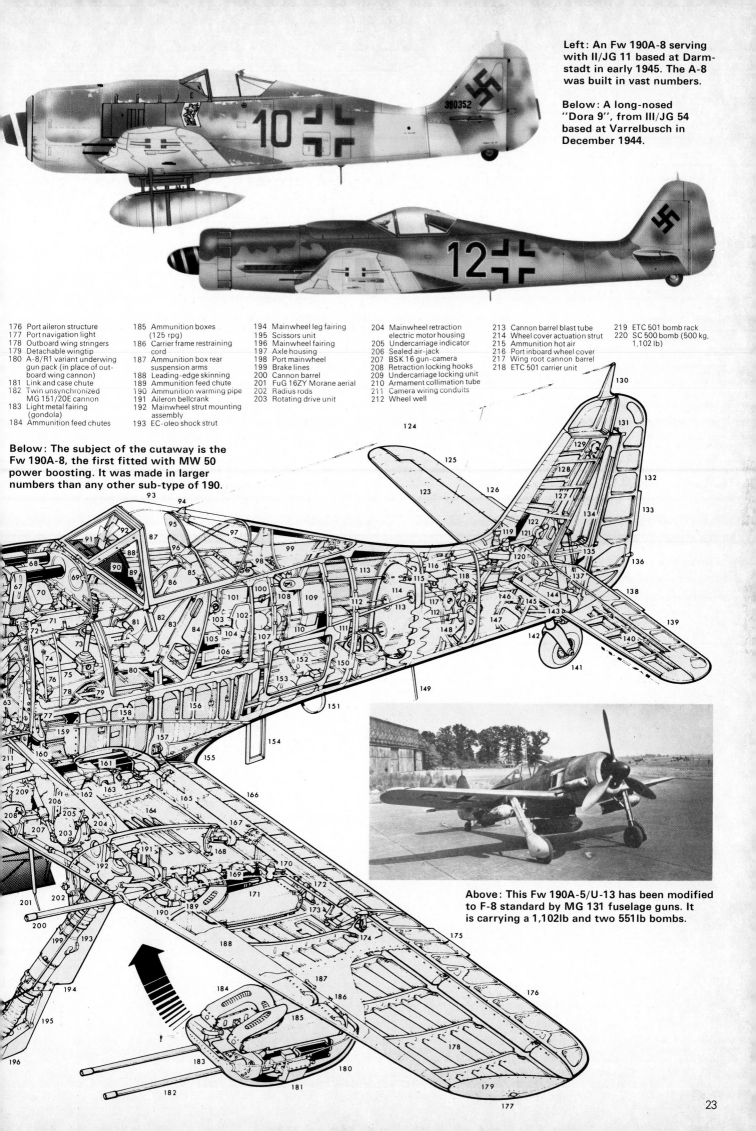

Left: An Fw 190A-8 serving with II/JG 11 based at Darmstadt in early 1945. The A-8 was built in vast numbers.

Below: A long-nosed "Dora 9", from III/JG 54 based at Varrelbusch in December 1944.

176 Port aileron structure
177 Port navigation light
178 Outboard wing stringers
179 Detachable wingtip
180 A-8/R1 variant underwing gun pack (in place of outboard wing cannon)
181 Link and case chute
182 Twin unsynchronized MG 151/20E cannon
183 Light metal fairing (gondola)
184 Ammunition feed chutes

185 Ammunition boxes (125 rpg)
186 Carrier frame restraining cord
187 Ammunition box rear suspension arms
188 Leading-edge skinning
189 Ammunition feed chute
190 Ammunition warming pipe
191 Aileron bellcrank
192 Mainwheel strut mounting assembly
193 EC-oleo shock strut

194 Mainwheel leg fairing
195 Scissors unit
196 Mainwheel fairing
197 Axle housing
198 Port mainwheel
199 Brake lines
200 Cannon barrel
201 FuG 16ZY Morane aerial
202 Radius rods
203 Rotating drive unit

204 Mainwheel retraction electric motor housing
205 Undercarriage indicator
206 Sealed air-jack
207 BSK 16 gun-camera
208 Retraction locking hooks
209 Undercarriage locking unit
210 Armament collimation tube
211 Camera wiring conduits
212 Wheel well

213 Cannon barrel blast tube
214 Wheel cover actuation strut
215 Ammunition hot air
216 Port inboard wheel cover
217 Wing root cannon barrel
218 ETC 501 carrier unit

219 ETC 501 bomb rack
220 SC 500 bomb (500 kg, 1,102 lb)

Below: The subject of the cutaway is the Fw 190A-8, the first fitted with MW 50 power boosting. It was made in larger numbers than any other sub-type of 190.

Above: This Fw 190A-5/U-13 has been modified to F-8 standard by MG 131 fuselage guns. It is carrying a 1,102lb and two 551lb bombs.

1: Fw 190A-5/U8 of I Gruppe, Schnellkampfgeschwader (SKG) 10, based at Poix, France, in the summer of 1943. The A-5/U8 was modified to carry a single 550lb (250kg) bomb, and this aircraft has a temporary matt black finish for dawn/dusk fighter-bomber attacks on England.

2: Fw 190A-3 of Ergänzungsjagdgeschwader (EJG, replacement fighter group) 1, based at Bad Albling, in May 1945, where this early model had been relegated to service as a fighter trainer.

3: Fw 190A-5 of II Gruppe of Jagdgeschwader (JG) 54 "Grünherz", based at Petseri, Estonia, in spring 1944. Inset is JG 54's Grünherz emblem.

4: Fw 190A-4/U3 of the Gefechtsverband (battle formation) Druschel, II Gruppe, Schlachtgeschwader (Sch.G.) 1, during operations in the Kursk salient in the summer of 1943. The A-4/U3 was another Jabo (fighter-bomber) conversion equipped to carry a single 550lb (250kg) bomb.

5: Fw 190A-6/R11 of 1 Staffel, Nachtjagdgruppe (NJG) 10, based at Werneuchen in the summer of 1944. The A-6 series Fw 190s introduced a new, lighter wing and standardised on an armament of two MG 17s in the fuselage and four wing-mounted 20mm MG 151 cannon. They were intended principally for service on the Eastern Front, and the R11 was an all-weather fighter version with autopilot and heated windscreen.

Above: The replacement of the original radial engine with a 12-cylinder in-line Junkers Jumo gave a distinctive new look to the Fw 190, the D-series models being dubbed Langenasen (long-nose) Dora, and the initial production D-9, or "Dora-9" restored the type's speed advantage, even over the P-51D Mustang. The first examples were delivered in August 1944, and a total of between 650 and 700 D-series Fw 190s had been completed by the time of Germany's surrender. The early cockpit canopy was replaced by a blown canopy at an early stage in production. Armament of the D-9 comprised two 13mm MG 131s mounted above the engine and a 20mm MG 151/20 cannon in each wing root; a 1,100lb (500kg) bomb could be carried under the fuselage.

1: Fw 190D-9 of 1.Staffel, Jagdgruppe 10, based at Redlin, February 1945.

2: This D-9 of 10./JG 54 crashed at Wemmel, Belgium, on January 1, 1945.

3: Fw 190D-9 of II/JG 26 "Schlageter", based at Nordhorn in January 1945.

4: Stab/JG 4 D-9, Babenhausen, early 1945, with "Defence of Reich" bands.

5: "Dora-9" of III/JG 2 "Richthofen", based at Altenstadt, December 1944.

6: A captured D-9 in service with a Russian fighter regiment, spring 1945.

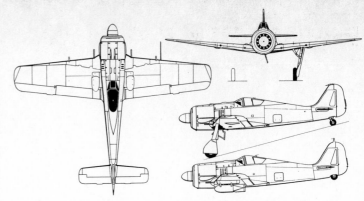

► **Weights:** Empty (A-8, F-8) 7,055lb (3200kg); (D-9) 7,720lb (3500kg); (Ta 152H-1) 7,940lb (3600kg); loaded (A-8, F-8) 10,800lb (4900kg); (D-9) 10,670lb (4840kg); (Ta 152H-1) 12,125lb (5500kg).

Performance: Maximum speed (with boost) (A-8, F-8) 408mph (653km/h); (D-9) 440mph (704km/h); (Ta 152H-1) 472mph (755km/h); initial climb (A-8, F-8) 2,350ft (720m)/min; (D-9, Ta 152) about 3,300ft (1000m)/min; service ceiling (A-8, F-8) 37,400ft (11,410m); (D-9) 32,810ft (10,000m); (Ta 152H-1) 49,215ft (15,000m); range on internal fuel (A-8, F-8 and D-9) about 560 miles (900km); (Ta 152H-1), 745 miles (1200km).

Armament: (A-8, F-8) two 13mm MG 131 above engine, two 20mm MG 151/20 in wing roots and two MG 151/20 or 30mm MK 108 in outer wings; (D-9) as above, or without outer MG 151/20s, with provision for 30mm MK 108 firing through propeller hub; (Ta 152H-1) one 30mm MK 108 and two inboard MG 151/20 (sometimes outboard MG 151/20s as well); bomb load (A-8, D-9) one 1,100lb (500kg) on centreline; (F-8) one 3,968lb (1800kg) on centreline; (Ta 152H-1) (some reconnaissance H-models unarmed).

History: First flight (Fw 190V1) June 1, 1939, (production Fw 190A-1) September 1940, (Fw 190D) late 1942.

Users: Croatia, Germany (Luftwaffe), Slovakia, Turkey; post-war, Argentina, France (Armée de l'Air, Aéronavale).

Development: Though flown well before World War II this trim little fighter was unknown to the Allies and caused a nasty surprise when first met over France in early 1941. Indeed, it was so far superior to the bigger and more sluggish Spitfire V that for the first time the RAF felt not only outnumbered but beaten technically. In June 1942 an Fw 190A-3 landed by mistake in England, and the Focke-Wulf was discovered to be even better than expected. It was faster than any Allied fighter in service, had far heavier armament (at that time the standard was two 7·92mm MG 17s over the engine, two of the previously unknown Mauser cannon inboard and two 20mm MG FF outboard), was immensely strong, had excellent power of manoeuvre and good pilot view. It was also an extremely small target, much lighter than any Allied fighter and had a stable widetrack landing gear (unlike the Bf 109). Altogether it gave Allied pilots and designers an inferiority complex. Though it never supplanted the 109, it was subsequently made in a profusion of different versions by many factories.

The A series included many fighter and fighter bomber versions, some having not only the increasingly heavy internal armament but also two or four 20mm cannon or two 30mm in underwing fairings. Most had an emergency power boost system, using MW 50 (methanol/water) or GM-1 (nitrous oxide) injection, or both. Some carried torpedoes, others were two-seaters, and a few had autopilots for bad weather and night interceptions. The F series were close-support attack aircraft, some having the Panzerblitz array of R4M rockets for tank-busting (also lethal against heavy bombers). There were over 40 other special armaments, and some versions had armoured leading edges for ramming Allied bombers. The G was another important series of multi-role fighter/dive bombers, but by 1943 the main effort was devoted to what the RAF called the "long-nosed 190", the 190D. This went into production in the autumn of 1944, after much development, as the Fw 190D-9 ("Dora 9"). This was once more the fastest fighter in the sky and the later D-models were redesignated Ta 152 in honour of the director of Focke-Wulf's design team, Dipl Ing Kurt Tank. The early 152C series were outstandingly formidable, but the long-span H sacrificed guns for speed and height. Tank himself easily outpaced a flight of P-51D Mustangs which surprised him on a test flight; but only ten of the H sub-type had flown when the war ended. Altogether 20,051 Fw 190s were delivered, plus a small number of Ta 152s (67, excluding development aircraft). It is curious that the Bf 109, a much older and less attractive design with many shortcomings, should have been made in greater quantity and flown by nearly all the Luftwaffe's aces.

In 1945 the Fw 190A-5 was put into production at an underground plant in France managed by SNCASO. By 1946 a total of 64 had been delivered.

Above: Three-view of Fw 190A-3; lower side view, A-4/U-1.

Below: The culminating fighter in the whole family was the Ta 152H, a fabulous performer at high altitude. The fifth example is seen having its compass swung at Cottbus in 1945.

Above: The second production version of the Ta 152 was the C-series, without the long-span wing (photo shows Ta 152C V7, a Ta 152C-0/R11). This had a normal armament of one 30mm MK 108 and four MG 151 20mm, and flew in December 1944.

Below: A row of Fw 190A-4 fighters with pilots at cockpit readiness, on a French airfield in 1943. This mottled camouflage was unusual on fighter 190s at this time, though it was occasionally seen on Jabo 190s bombing English coasts.

Focke-Wulf Fw 200 Condor

Fw 200C-0 to C-8

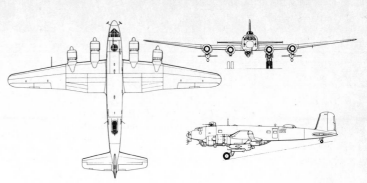

Origin: Focke-Wulf Flugzeugbau GmbH, in partnership with Hamburger Flugzeugbau (Blohm und Voss).

Type: Maritime reconnaissance bomber and (C-6 to -8) missile launcher, many used as transports.

Engines: Usually four 1,200hp BMW-Bramo Fafnir 323R-2 nine-cylinder radials.

Dimensions: Span 107ft 9½in (30·855m); length 76ft 11½in (23·46m); height 20ft 8in (6·3m).

Weights: (C-3/U-4) empty 28,550lb (12,951kg); loaded 50,045lb (22,700kg).

Performance: Maximum speed (C-3) 224mph (360km/h); (C-8) 205mph (330km/h); initial climb, about 656ft (200m)/min; service ceiling 19,030ft (5800m); range with standard fuel, 2,206 miles (3550km).

Armament: Typical C-3/C-8, one forward dorsal turret with one 15mm MG 151/15 (or 20mm MG 151/20 or one 7·92mm MG 15), one 20mm MG 151/20 manually aimed at front of ventral gondola, three 7·92mm MG 15 manually aimed at rear of ventral gondola and two beam windows (beam guns sometimes being 13mm MG 131) and one 13mm MG 131 in aft dorsal position; maximum bomb load of 4,626lb (2100kg) carried in gondola and beneath outer wings (C-6, C-8, two Hs 293 guided missiles carried under outboard nacelles).

History: First flight (civil prototype) 27 July 1937; (Fw 200C-0) January 1940; final delivery (C-8) February 1944.

User: (Fw 200C series) Germany (Luftwaffe).

Development: Planned solely as a long-range commercial transport for the German airline Deutsche Luft Hansa, the prewar Fw·200 prototypes set up impressive record flights to New York and Tokyo and attracted export orders from Denmark, Brazil, Finland and Japan. Transport prototype and production versions were also used by Hitler and Himmler as VIP executive machines and several later variants were also converted as

Above: The Fw 200C-8/U10, the final sub-type, with Hs 293s.

special transports. In 1938 the Japanese asked for one Condor converted for use as a long-range ocean reconnaissance machine. The resulting Fw 200V-10 prototype introduced a ventral gondola and led to the Fw 200C-0 as the prototype of a Luftwaffe aircraft which had never been requested or planned and yet which was to prove a most powerful instrument of war. Distinguished by long-chord cowlings, twin-wheel main gears (because of the increased gross weight) and a completely new armament and equipment fit, the C-0 led to the C-1, used operationally from June 1940 by KG 40 at Bordeaux-Mérignac. By September 1940 this unit alone had sunk over 90,000 tons of Allied shipping and for the next three years the C-series Condors were in Churchill's words, "the scourge of the Atlantic". But, though the Fw 200 family continued to grow in equipment and lethality, the Allies fought back with long-range Coastal Command aircraft, escort carriers and CAM (Catapult-Armed Merchantman) fighters and by mid-1944 surviving Condors were being forced into transport roles on other fronts. Total production was 276 and one of the fundamental failings of the Condor was structural weakness, catastrophic wing and fuselage failures occurring not only in the air but even on the ground, on take-off or landing.

Left: An early Fw 200C-3 serving with KG 40 at Bordeaux-Mérignac and Cognac, west France, in the summer of 1941.

Below: A modified version was the Fw 200C-3/U2, whose bombing accuracy was increased by the Lotfe 7D sight.

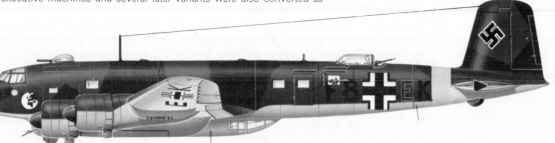

Gotha Go 145

Go 145A, B and C

Origin: Gothaer Waggonfabrik AG, Gotha; production subcontracted to Ago, BFW (Messerschmitt) and Focke-Wulf; built under licence by CASA, Spain, and Demag, Turkey.
Type: Primary trainer, but see text.
Engine: 240hp Argus As 10C inverted-vee-8 aircooled.
Dimensions: Span 29ft 6¼in (9·00m); length 28ft 6½in (8·70m); height 9ft 6¼in (2·90m).
Weights: Empty (A) 1,940lb (880kg); maximum 3,043lb (1380kg).
Performance: Maximum speed 132mph (212km/h); typical range 404 miles (650km).
History: First flight February 1934; service delivery 1935; final delivery (Germany) not before 1943, (Spain) about 1945.
Users: Bulgaria, Croatia, Germany, Slovakia, Spain, Turkey (possibly others).

Development: The Go 145 is another of the many types of aircraft which made a giant contribution to World War II yet today are almost forgotten. This biplane trainer was not only manufactured in enormous numbers – at least 9,965 in Germany, plus more than 1,000 in Spain and Turkey – but it also became a combat type and stayed in the very forefront of battle from 1942 until the final collapse in 1945. The basic machine was wooden, with fabric covering, but it was so tractable and strong that, as well as equipping roughly half the elementary flying training schools for the Luftwaffe from 1936 onwards, the Go 145 was chosen to equip the night harassment squadrons on the Eastern Front (triggered by the maddening pinpricks of the Soviet Po-2). At first called Störkampfstaffeln, they were progressively expanded and upgraded, and Go 145 output was increased to meet the demand. In October 1943, after ten months, they were reclassified NSGr, the same as other night attack units, and many hundreds of 145s equipped six whole geschwader, plus the Ost-Flieger Gruppe. They carried various guns, light bombs, loudspeakers and even rockets. The only other sub-type in Luftwaffe use was the 145C gunnery trainer.

Below: A Go 145A flying dual at a Luftwaffe A/B Schule.

Gotha Go 242 and 244

Go 242A, B and C, Go 244B and Ka 430

Origin: Gothaer Waggonfabrik AG, Kassel; production subcontracted.
Type: Transport glider (244, transport aeroplane).
Engines: (244) two 700hp Gnome-Rhône 14M4/5 14-cylinder radials.
Dimensions: Span 80ft 4½in (24·50m); length 51ft 10in (15·81m); height (242) 14ft 4¼in (4·40m), (244) 15ft 5in (14·70m).
Weights: Empty (242A-2) 7,056lb (3200kg), (244B-2) 11,245lb (5100kg); maximum (242A-2) 15,655lb (7100kg), (244B-2) 17,198lb (7800kg).
Performance: Maximum speed (242 on tow) 149mph (240km/h), (244) 180mph (290km/h); maximum range at sea level (244) 373 miles (600km).
History: First flight (242) early 1941, (244) late 1941, (430) 1944.
User: Germany.

Development: This family of tactical transports was the only Gotha of World War II (other than the Go 145 designed much earlier). The 242 was a simple machine with nacelle of steel tube and fabric lifted and controlled by wooden wings and tail. It could carry 21 troops or light vehicles and stores loaded through the hinged rear fairing, took off on jettisonable wheels and landed on skids. The tug was usually the He 111, but the Bf 110 could cope on a good airfield; sometimes the He 111Z was used, and experiments were made with solid rocket ATO motors. Air bottles worked lift spoilers and flaps. Variants were A-1 (freight only), A-2 (troops), B-1 (nosewheel),

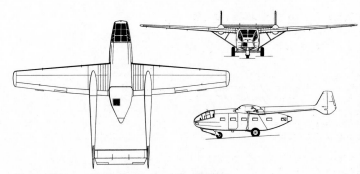

Above: Three-view of a typical Go 242B-1.

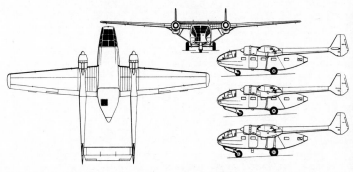

Above: Go 244B-1 (middle) with Go 244 V1 (top) and B-2 (lower).

B-2 (oleo landing gear), B-3 and -4 (paratroop), B-5 (dual trainer) and C-1 (flying boat). The number built was 1,528, in 1941–43, of which 133 were fitted with engines (almost always the French GR 14M, but sometimes the BMW 132Z or Russian M-25A) to become the Go 244. The 244B-1 to B-5 were conversions of the same 242 models, but they proved vulnerable in the Soviet Union and North Africa and were soon scrapped. The Ka 430, named for Gotha's lead designer Albert Kalkert, was a refined development with single tailboom. Experiments with the prototype included rocket braking.

Left: The Go 244B-1 was usually a conversion of the Go 242B-1 glider. The powered version was not a great success.

Heinkel He 51

He 51A-1, B-2 and C-1

Origin: Ernst Heinkel AG; production see text.
Type: Single-seat fighter (B-2) reconnaissance seaplane; (C-1) land ground attack.
Engine: One 750hp BMW VI 7·3Z vee-12 water-cooled.
Dimensions: Span 36ft 1in (11m); length 27ft 6¾in (8·4m); (B-2) about 31ft; height 10ft 6in (3·2m); (B-2) about 11ft.
Weights: (A-1), empty 3,223lb (1462kg); loaded 4,189lb (1900kg).
Performance: Maximum speed (A-1) 205mph (330km/h); initial climb 1,969ft (600m)/min; service ceiling 24,610ft (7500m); range 242 miles (390km).
Armament: Standard, two 7·92mm Rheinmetall MG 17 synchronised above fuselage; (B-2) same plus underwing racks for up to six 22lb (10kg) bombs; (C-1) same plus underwing racks for four 110lb (50kg) bombs.
History: First flight (He 49a) November 1932; (He 49b) February 1933; (He 51A-0) May 1933; service delivery of A-1, July 1934.
Users: Germany, Spain.
Development: Gradually, as the likelihood of Allied legal action receded, Heinkel dared to build aircraft that openly contravened the Versailles Treaty. The most startling was the He 37, obviously a prototype fighter, which in 1928 achieved 194mph, or 20mph faster than the RAF Bulldog which was still a year away from service. Land and seaplane versions led to a succession of He 49 fighter prototypes in the 1930s and these in turn provided the basis for the refined He 51. After the Ar 65 this was the first fighter ordered into

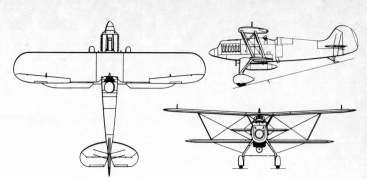

Above: Three-view of He 51C-1 (the B-1 was very similar).

production by the Reichsluftfahrtministerium for the reborn Luftwaffe. Though the initial order for He 51A-1s was only 75, Heinkel was unused to such an order and many were built under licence by Ago, Erla, Arado and Fieseler – which were also fast tooling for their own designs. In March 1935 the Luftwaffe was publicly announced, and JG1 "Richthofen" fighter squadron was combat-ready at Döberitz with its new Heinkels. In November 1936, 36 He 51A-1s went to Spain with the Legion Kondor, giving a sufficiently good showing for the Nationalists to buy at least 30 from Heinkel. There followed a total of 50 of various He 51B seaplane versions, the 38 B-2s being for service aboard cruisers. The final batch comprised 79 C-1 ground attack fighters, of which 28 served in Spain. The He 51 was still in active service in September 1939, operating in the close-support role in Poland, and remained as an advanced trainer until 1943.

Right: By the start of World War II most He 51 fighters had been assigned as advanced trainers to Jagdfliegerschulen (fighter-pilot schools). This He 51B-1 survived as late as 1942 at the main Balkan school A/B 123 at Agram (Zagreb). By then, Luftwaffe pilot training was disintegrating.

Heinkel He 59

He 59B, C, D, E and N

Origin: Ernst Heinkel AG, Marienehe; production subcontracted to Walter Bachmann AG, Ribnitz; also some built under licence (about 1935) by Arado Flugzeugwerke.
Type: See text.
Engines: Two 660hp BMW VI vee-12 water-cooled.
Dimensions: Span 77ft 9½in (23·70m); length (most) 57ft 1¾in (17·40m); height 23ft 3¾in (7·10m).
Weights: (C-2) empty 13,702lb (6215kg); maximum 19,842lb (9000kg).
Performance: Maximum speed (typical) 134mph (215km/h); extreme range with max fuel 1,087 miles (1750km).
Armament: Three or four 7·92mm MG 15 (later, MG 81) manually aimed from bow, dorsal and ventral positions; many sub-types carried at least one 20mm MG FF, and most B-2 having provision for 2,205lb (1000kg) of mines, bombs or other ordnance.
History: First flight (landplane second prototype) September 1931; service delivery (He 59A-0) August 1932; final delivery from new, probably 1936.
Users: Finland, Germany, Romania.

Above: The He 59B-2 reconnaissance and torpedo bomber.

Development: One of the first military aircraft built in Germany after the Versailles Treaty (which it openly contravened), the He 59 was destined to serve in an extraordinary variety of roles long after its antiquated appearance might have suggested it was obsolescent. In fact like many Axis warplanes it proved to be more and more useful, and though few were left by 1943 there were in that year at least 18 units operating different He 59 sub-types in mining, ground attack, rescue, transport, electronic warfare and psy-war missions. It was planned as a land or seaplane torpedo bomber, but in 1932 entered service mainly in the reconnaissance role. In the Kondor Legion in Spain it made heavy bombing attacks on Republican ports (often after a quiet gliding run-in at night), and in 1940 more than 180 were intensively used for all manner of missions – the most daring of which was the flying-in of ten He 59C-2 rescue transports to the Waal at Rotterdam to disgorge 60 troops who captured the city's main bridge. Most mining missions in 1939–43 were flown by B-2 or B-3 versions, but many were rebuilt as He 59N radio/radar trainers.

Left: This He 59N navigation trainer is typical of the oft-rebuilt He 59 seaplanes late in the war (when only a few survived). Some retained armament, while others served as trials platforms and trainers for airborne electronic systems.

Heinkel He 111

He 111 B series, E series, H series and P series

Origin: Ernst Heinkel AG; also built in France on German account by SNCASO; built under licence by Fabrica de Avione SET, Romania, and CASA, Spain.

Type: Four-seat or five-seat medium bomber (later, torpedo bomber, glider tug and missile launcher).

Engines: (He 111H-3) two 1,200hp Junkers Jumo 211D-2 12-cylinder inverted-vee liquid-cooled; (He 111P-2) two 1,100hp Daimler-Benz DB 601A-1 12-cylinder inverted-vee liquid-cooled.

Dimensions: (H-3) Span 74ft 1¾in (22·6m); length 53ft 9½in (16·4m); height 13ft 1½in (4m).

Weights: Empty (H-3) 17,000lb (7720kg); (P-2) 17,640lb (8000kg); maximum loaded (H-3) 30,865lb (14,000kg); (P-2) 29,762lb (13,500kg).

Performance: Maximum speed (H-3) 258mph (415km/h); (P-2) 242mph (390km/h) at 16,400ft (5000m) (at maximum weight, neither version could exceed 205mph, 330km/h); climb to 14,765ft (4500m) 30–35min at normal gross weight, 50min at maximum; service ceiling (both) around 25,590ft (7800m) at normal gross weight, under 16,400ft (5000m) at maximum; range with maximum bomb load (both) about 745 miles (1200km).

Armament: (P-2) 7·92mm Rheinmetall MG 15 machine gun on manual mountings in nosecap, open dorsal position and ventral gondola; (H-3) same, plus fixed forward-firing MG 15 or 17, two MG 15s in waist windows and (usually) 20mm MG FF cannon in front of ventral gondola and (sometimes)

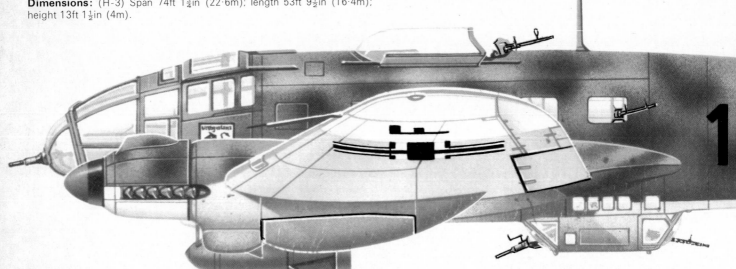

Heinkel He III H-3 cutaway drawing key:

1 Starboard navigation light
2 Starboard aileron
3 Lattice ribs
4 Front spar
5 Rear spar
6 Aileron tab
7 Starboard flap
8 Outboard fuel tank (220 gal/ 1,000 litres capacity)
9 Wing centre section/outer panel break line
10 Inboard fuel tank (154 gal/ 700 litres capacity) inboard of nacelle
11 Oil tank cooling louvres
12 Oil cooler air intake
13 Supercharger air intake
14 Three-blade VDM propeller
15 Airscrew pitch-change mechanism
16 Junkers Jumo 211D-1 12-cylinder inverted-vee liquid-cooled engine
17 Exhaust manifold
18 Nose-mounted 7·92mm MG 15 machine gun
19 Ikaria ball-and-socket gun mounting (offset to starboard)
20 Bomb sight housing (offset to starboard)
21 Starboard mainwheel
22 Rudder pedals
23 Bomb aimer's prone pad
24 Additional 7·92mm MG 15 machine gun (fitted by forward maintenance units)
25 Repeater compass
26 Bomb aimer's folding seat
27 Control wheel
28 Throttles
29 Pilot's seat
30 Retractable auxiliary windscreen (for use when pilot's seat in elevated position)
31 Sliding roof hatch
32 Forward fuselage bulkhead
33 Double-frame station
34 Port ESAC bomb bay (vertical stowage)
35 Fuselage windows (blanked)
36 Central gangway between bomb bays
37 Double-frame station
38 Direction finder
39 Dorsal gunner's (forward) sliding canopy
40 Dorsal 7·92mm MG 15 machine gun
41 Dorsal gunner's cradle seat
42 FuG 10 radio equipment
43 Fuselage window
44 Armoured bulkhead (8mm)
45 Aerial mast
46 Bomb flares
47 Unarmoured bulkhead
48 Rear fuselage access cut-out
49 Port 7·92mm beam MG 15 machine gun
50 Dinghy stowage
51 Fuselage frames
52 Stringers
53 Starboard tailplane
54 Aerial
55 Starboard elevator
56 Fin front spar
57 Fin structure
58 Rudder balance
59 Fin rear spar/rudder post
60 Rudder construction
61 Rudder tab
62 Tab actuator
63 Remotely-controlled 7·92 mm MG 17 machine gun in tailcone (fitted to some aircraft only)
64 Rear navigation light
65 Elevator tab
66 Elevator structure
67 Tailplane main spar
68 Tailplane front spar
69 Semi-retractable tailwheel
70 Tailwheel shock-absorber
71 Rudder control linkage
72 Fuselage/tail frame
73 Rudder control cables
74 Elevator push-pull control rods
75 Master compass
76 Observation window fairing
77 Glazed observation window in floor

Below: The subject of the cutaway drawing is the He 111H-3, a member of what became by far the most important He 111 family. Powered by the Jumo 211 engine (the final sub-type, a saboteur transport in 1944, had the 1,776hp Jumo 213) the H-series eventually ran to a unique 23 basic sub-models, each with its own variations.

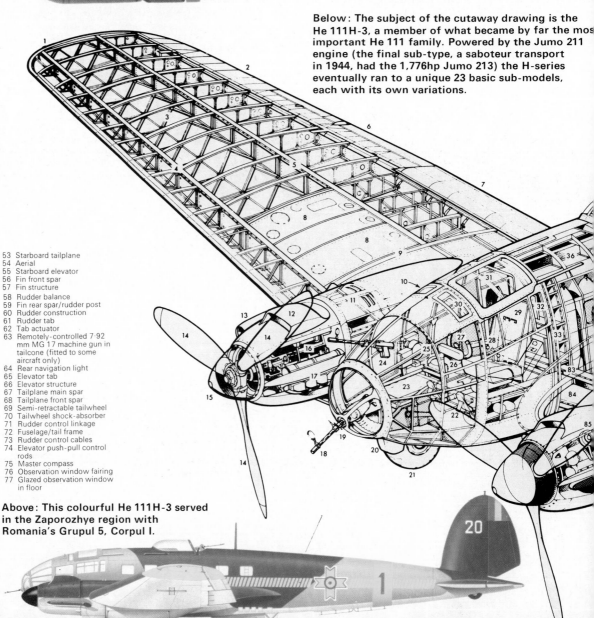

Above: This colourful He 111H-3 served in the Zaporozhye region with Romania's Grupul 5, Corpul I.

fixed rear-firing MG 17 in extreme tail; internal bomb load up to 4,410lb (2000kg) in vertical cells, stored nose-up; external bomb load (at expense of internal) one 4,410lb (2000kg) on H-3, one or two 1,102lb (500kg) on others; later marks carried one or two 1,686lb (765kg) torpedoes, Bv 246 glide missiles, Hs 293 rocket missiles, Fritz X radio-controlled glide bombs or one FZG-76 ("V-1") cruise missile.

Below: Painted in North African camouflage, this He 111H-6 had by August 1943 been pushed back to Ottana, Sardinia. Serving with 2/KG 26, it has two forward-aimed MG FF 20mm cannon for attacks on shipping, heavy external racks (two 1,102lb are shown) and extra beam and tail guns.

Above: Dubbed "Die Späten" (the Spade) by its crews, the broad-winged Heinkel cast its black shadow over virtually all Europe. In 1939 it was a most modern bomber, but there followed seven years of fumbling modifications which never overcame the need for a modern bomber as a replacement.

78	Ventral aft-firing 7·92mm MG 15 machine gun in tail of 'Sterbebett' ('Death-bed') bath	83	Forward spar carry-through
		84	Oil cooler
		85	Anti-vibration engine mount
		86	Oil tank
79	Ventral bath entry hatch	87	Engine bearer
80	Ventral gunner's prone pad	88	Exhaust flame-damper shroud
81	Forward-firing 20mm Oerlikon MG FF cannon (for anti-shipping operations)	89	Radiator air intake
		90	Radiator bath
82	Rear spar carry-through	91	Port mainwheel
92	Mainwheel leg	99	Flap control rod
93	Retraction mechanism	100	Landing light
94	Mainwheel door (outer)	101	Pitot head
95	Multi-screw wing attachment	102	Pitot head heater/wing leading-edge de-icer
96	Trailing-aerial tube (to starboard of ventral bath)	103	Flap and aileron coupling
97	Rear spar attachment	104	Flap structure
98	Port outboard fuel tank (220 gal/1,000 litres capacity)	105	Aileron tab
		106	Tab actuator
		107	Rear spar
108	Forward spar		
109	Port aileron		
110	Port navigation light		

► **History:** First flight (He 111V1 prototype) 24 February 1935; (pre-production He 111B-0) August 1936; (production He 111B-1) 30 October 1936; (first He 111E series) January 1938; (first production He 111P-1) December 1938; (He 111H-1) January or February 1939; final delivery (He 111H-23) October 1944; (Spanish C.2111) late 1956.
Users: China, Germany (Luftwaffe, Luft Hansa), Hungary, Iraq, Romania, Spain, Turkey.

Development: A natural twin-engined outgrowth of the He 70, the first He 111 was a graceful machine with elliptical wings and tail, secretly flown as a bomber but revealed to the world a year later as a civil airliner. Powered by 660hp BMW VI engines, it had typical armament of three manually aimed machine guns but the useful bomb load of 2,200lb (1000kg) stowed nose-up in eight cells in the centre fuselage. In 1937 a number of generally similar machines secretly flew photo-reconnaissance missions over Britain, France and the Soviet Union, in the guise of airliners of Deutsche Luft Hansa. In the same year the He 111B-1 came into Luftwaffe service, with two 880hp Daimler-Benz DB 600C engines, while a vast new factory was built at Oranienburg solely to make later versions. In February 1937 operations began with the Legion Kondor in Spain, with considerable success, flight performance being improved in the B-2 by 950hp DB 600CG engines which were retained in the C series. The D was faster, with the 1,000hp Jumo 211A-1, also used in the He 111 F in which a new straight-edged wing was introduced. To a considerable degree the success of the early elliptical-winged He 111 bombers in Spain misled the Luftwaffe into considering that nothing could withstand the onslaught of their huge fleets of medium bombers. These aircraft — the trim Do 17, the broad-winged He 111 and the high-performance Ju 88 — were all extremely advanced by the standards of the mid-1930s when they were designed. They were faster than the single-seat fighters of that era and, so the argument went, therefore did not need much defensive armament. So the three machine guns carried by the first He 111 bombers in 1936 stayed unchanged until, in the Battle of Britain, the He 111 was hacked down with ease, its only defence being its toughness and ability to come back after being shot to pieces. The inevitable result was that more and more defensive guns were added, needing a fifth or even a sixth crew-member. Coupled with incessant growth in equipment and armour the result was deteriorating performance, so that the record-breaker of 1936–38 became the lumbering sitting duck of 1942–45. Yet the He 111 was built in ever-greater numbers, virtually all the later sub-types being

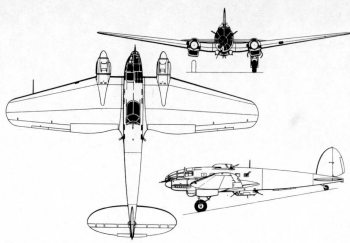

Above: A fairly late bomber variant, the He 111H-16.

members of the prolific H-series. Variations were legion, including versions with large barrage-balloon deflectors, several kinds of missiles (including a V-1 tucked under the left wing root), while a few were completed as saboteur transports. The most numerous version was the H-6, and the extraordinary He 111Z (Zwilling) glider tug of 1942 consisted of two H-6s joined by a common centre wing carrying a fifth engine. Right to the end of the war the RLM and German industry failed to find a replacement for the old "Spaten" (spade). and the total produced in Germany and Romania was at least 6,086 and possibly more than 7,000. Merlin-engined C.2111 versions continued in production in Spain until 1956.

Below: Luftwaffe armourers hand-pulled heavy bombs far more than did those of the RAF (though this may have been due to the fact that more RAF bombers operated from permanent bases). This 1,102lb SC500 is going to be hung externally as one of a pair under an He 111H-6 of KG 55 (not that in the picture). The photo was taken on the Eastern Front in June 1941.

Heinkel He 115

He 115A, B, C, D and E

Origin: Ernst Heinkel AG, Marienehe.
Type: Multi-role seaplane, see text.
Engines: Two BMW 132 nine-cylinder radials, (B-1) usually 865hp 132N, (C-1) usually 970hp 132K.
Dimensions: Span 73ft 1in (22·275m); length (typical) 56ft 9½in (17·30 m); height (typical) 21ft 7¾in (6·60m).
Weights: Empty (B-1) 14,748lb (6690kg); maximum 22,928lb (10,400kg).
Performance: Maximum speed (B, C, typical) 203mph (327km/h); maximum range (full weapons) 1,300 miles (2090km), (max fuel) 2,050 miles (3300km).
Armament: See text.
History: First flight (prototype) about October 1936; service delivery (115A-0) July 1937; final delivery about July 1944.
Users: Bulgaria, Finland, Germany, Norway, Sweden, UK (RAF).

Development: A wholly outstanding machine in all respects, the 115 was tough, beautiful to fly at speeds down to 75 knots, and carried a substantial load at relatively high speeds. In 1938 the prototype was specially stream-lined to set class records, and the first Luftwaffe operational version, the A-1,

Above: A Weser-built He 115B-0 of 1939, one of the earliest versions for service use. Survivors were later re-equipped.

was sold to Norway and Sweden with small changes. Most A-models carried one LTF 5 or 6b torpedo or up to 2,205lb (1000kg) of mines or other stores, and the nose and rear cockpits each had a 7·92mm or 0·303in gun. By 1939 long-range B models were in production, which could carry the new 2,028lb (920kg) magnetic mine in addition to a 1,102lb (500kg) bomb load at a cruising speed of some 150mph. The B-2 had floats streng-thened for ice or snow. In April 1940 the Norwegian aircraft were engaged in fierce combat and made many bombing missions on German forces before the four survivors set out for Scotland. One of these was fitted with eight wing machine guns and used by the RAF on secret agent-dropping between Malta and North Africa. Another Norse escapee was used in Finland. In 1940 production centred on the C series, with many variants and often an MG 151 cannon in the nose. The single D had 1,600hp BMW 801 engines, and after being out of production 18 months a further 141 E-models were built in 1944 to bring the total past the 400 mark. Like the earlier versions the E-series were used for armed reconnaissance, minelaying, utility transport and casevac and even shallow dive bombing and torpedo bombing.

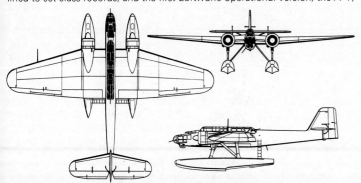

Left: Three-view of He 115B-1; later a nose cannon was added.

Heinkel He 177 Greif

He 177A-0 to A-5, He 277 and He 274

Origin: Ernst Heinkel AG; also built by Arado Flugzeugwerke.
Type: He 177, six-seat heavy bomber and missile carrier.
Engines: Two 2,950hp Daimler-Benz DB 610A-1/B-1, each comprising two inverted-vee-12 liquid-cooled engines geared to one propeller.
Dimensions: Span 103ft 1¾in (31·44m); length 72ft 2in (22m); height 21ft (6·4m).
Weights: Empty 37,038lb (16,800kg); loaded (A-5) 68,343lb (31,000kg).
Performance: Maximum speed (at 41,000lb, 18,615kg) 295mph (472 km/h); initial climb 853ft (260m)/min; service ceiling 26,500ft (7080m); range with FX or Hs 293 missiles (no bombs) about 3,107 miles (5000km).
Armament: (A-5/R2) one 7·92mm MG 81J manually aimed in nose, one 20mm MG 151 manually aimed at front of ventral gondola, one or two 13mm MG 131 in forward dorsal turret, one MG 131 in rear dorsal turret, one MG 151 manually aimed in tail and two MG 81 or one MG 131 manually aimed at rear of gondola; maximum internal bomb load 13,200lb (6000kg), seldom carried; external load, two Hs 293 guided missiles, FX 1400 guided bombs, mines or torpedoes (more if internal bay blanked off and racks added below it).
History: First flight (He 177V-1) 19 November 1939; (pre-production He 177A-0) November 1941; service delivery (A-1) March 1942; (A-5) February 1943; first flight (He 277V-1) December 1943; (He 274, alias AAS 01A) December 1945.
User: Germany (Luftwaffe).

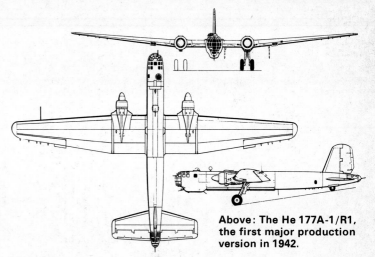

Above: The He 177A-1/R1, the first major production version in 1942.

Development: The Heinkel 177, Germany's biggest bomber programme in World War II, is remembered as possibly the most troublesome and un-satisfactory aircraft in military history, and it was only through dogged courage and persistence that large numbers were put into service. Much of the fault lay in the stupid 1938 requirement that the proposed heavy bomber and anti-ship aircraft should be capable of dive bombing. Certainly the wish to reduce drag by using coupled pairs of engines was mistaken, because no engines in bomber history have caught fire so often in normal cruising flight. Six of the eight prototypes crashed and many of the 35 pre-production A-0s (built mainly by Arado) were written off in take-off swings or in-flight fires. Arado built 130 A-1s, followed by 170 Heinkel-built A-3s and 826 A-5s with repositioned engines and longer fuselages. About 700 served on the Eastern Front, many having 50mm and 75mm guns for tank-busting; a few nervously bombed Britain in 400mph shallow dives, without any proper aiming of their bombs. So bothersome were these beasts that Goering forbade Heinkel to pester him any more with plans to use four separate engines, but Heinkel secretly flew the He 277, with four 1,750hp DB 603A, at Vienna, as the first of a major programme. The almost completely redesigned He 274 was a high-altitude bomber developed at the Farman factory at Suresnes, with four 1,850hp engines, a 145ft wing and twin fins. After the liberation it was readied for flight and flown at Orléans-Bricy.

Left: Main operational model was the A-5, of which 826 were built. This A-5/R2 has external racks for Fritz-X and Hs 293 guided missiles under its wings and on the centreline.

Heinkel He 162 Salamander

He 162A-2

Origin: Ernst Heinkel AG; first batch Vienna-Schwechat, production totally dispersed with underground assembly at Nordhausen (Mittelwerke), Bernberg (Junkers) and Rostock (Heinkel).

Type: Single-seat interceptor.

Engine: One 1,760lb (800kg) thrust BMW 003E-1 or E-2 Orkan single-shaft turbojet.

Dimensions: Span 23ft 7¾in (7·2m); length 29ft 8½in (9m); height 6ft 6½in (2–6m).

Weights: Empty 4,796lb (2180kg); loaded 5,940lb (2695kg).

Performance: Maximum speed 490mph (784km/h) at sea level, 522mph (835km/h) at 19,700ft (6000m); initial climb 4,200ft (1280m)/min; service ceiling 39,500ft (12,040m); range at full throttle 434 miles (695km) at altitude.

Armament: Early versions, two 30mm Rheinmetall MK 108 cannon with 50 rounds each; later production, two 20mm Mauser MG 151/20 with 120 rounds each.

History: First flight 6 December 1944; first delivery January 1945.

User: Germany (Luftwaffe).

Above: At one of the Heinkel plants an unpainted 162A-2 sits with canopy shattered in May 1945.

Development: Popularly called "Volksjäger" (People's Fighter), this incredible aircraft left behind so many conflicting impressions it is hard to believe the whole programme was started and finished in little more than six months. To appreciate the almost impossible nature of the programme, Germany was being pounded to rubble by fleets of Allied bombers that darkened the sky, and the aircraft industry and the Luftwaffe's fuel supplies were inexorably running down. Experienced aircrew had nearly all been killed, materials were in critically short supply and time had to be measured not in months but in days. So on 8 September 1944 the RLM issued a specification calling for a 750km/h jet fighter to be regarded as a piece of consumer goods and to be ready by 1 January 1945. Huge numbers of workers were organised to build it even before it was designed and Hitler Youth were hastily trained in primary gliders before being strapped into the new jet. Heinkel, which had built the world's first turbojet aircraft (He 178, flown 27 August 1939) and the first jet fighter (He 280 twin-jet, flown on its jet engines 2 April 1941) won a hasty competition with a tiny wooden machine with its engine perched on top and blasting between twin fins. Drawings were ready on 30 October 1944. The prototype flew in 37 days and plans were made for production to rise rapidly to 4,000 per month. Despite extreme difficulties, 300 of various sub-types had been completed by VE-day, with 800 more on the assembly lines. I/JG1 was operational at Leck, though without fuel. Despite many bad characteristics the 162 was a fighter of a futuristic kind, created in quantity far quicker than modern aircraft are even drawn on paper.

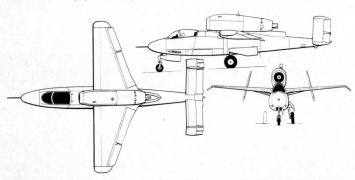

Above: Three-view of the mass-produced He 162A-2 Salamander.

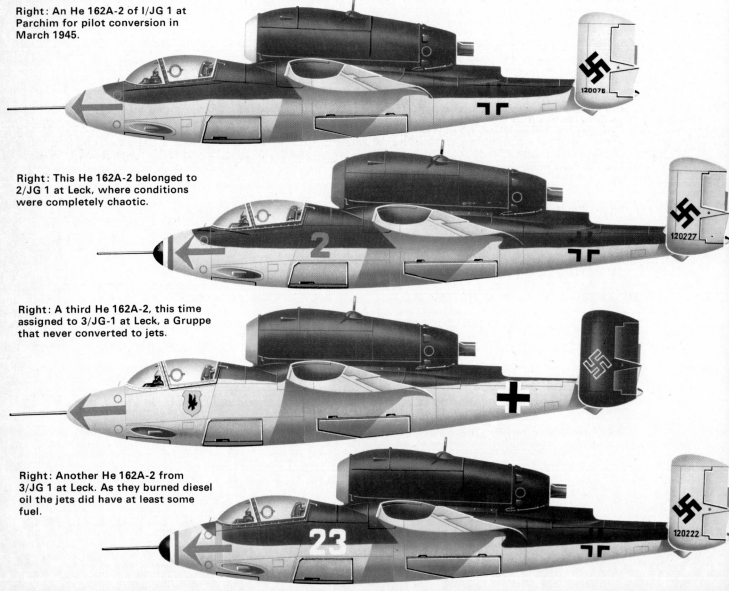

Right: An He 162A-2 of I/JG 1 at Parchim for pilot conversion in March 1945.

Right: This He 162A-2 belonged to 2/JG 1 at Leck, where conditions were completely chaotic.

Right: A third He 162A-2, this time assigned to 3/JG-1 at Leck, a Gruppe that never converted to jets.

Right: Another He 162A-2 from 3/JG 1 at Leck. As they burned diesel oil the jets did have at least some fuel.

Heinkel He 219 Uhu

He 219A-0 to A-7, B and C series

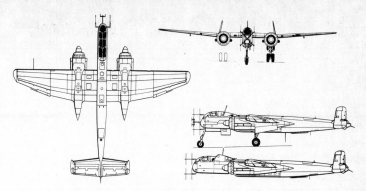

Origin: Ernst Heinkel AG.
Type: A series, two-seat night fighter.
Engines: Usually two 1,900hp Daimler-Benz DB 603G inverted-vee-12 liquid-cooled; other engines, see text.
Dimensions: (A-series) span 60ft 2in or 60ft 8in (18·5m); length (with aerials) 50ft 11¾in (15·54m); height 13ft 5½in (4·1m).
Weights: (A-7) empty 24,692lb (11,200kg); loaded 33,730lb (15,200kg).
Performance: (A-7) maximum speed 416mph (670km/h); initial climb 1,804ft (550m)/min; service ceiling 41,660ft (12,700m); range 1,243 miles (2000km).
Armament: Varied, see text.
History: First flight (219V-1) 15 November 1942; service delivery (prototypes) May 1943; (production 219A-1) November 1943.
User: Germany (Luftwaffe).

Above: Three-view of He 219A-5/R1; lower side view, the lengthened A-5/R4 with MG 131 in the rear cockpit for defence.

Development: Ernst Heinkel was the pioneer of gas-turbine jet aircraft, flying the He 178 on 27 August 1939 and the He 280 twin-jet fighter as a glider on 22 September 1940 and with its engines on 2 April 1941 (before the purely experimental Gloster E.28/39). But Heinkel was unable to build the extremely promising He 280 in quantity, which was fortunate for the Allies. He had no spare capacity for the He 219 either, which had excited little official interest when submitted as the P.1060 project in August 1940 as a high-speed fighter, bomber and torpedo carrier. It was only when RAF night attacks began to hurt, at the end of 1941, that he was asked to produce the 219 as a night fighter (Uhu meaning Owl). The He 219V-1, with 1,750hp DB 603AS and two MG 151/20 cannon, plus an MG 131 in the rear cockpit, was fast and extremely manoeuvrable and the test pilots at Rechlin were thrilled by it. Successive prototypes had much heavier armament and radar and 100 were ordered from five factories in Germany, Poland and Austria. The order was soon trebled and Luftwaffe enthusiasm was such that even the early prototypes were sent to Venlo, Holland, to form a special trials unit. The first six night sorties resulted in the claimed destruction of 20 RAF bombers, six of them the previously almost immune Mosquitoes! More than 15 different versions of the 219 then appeared, immediately proving outstandingly formidable. The A-2/R1 had 603As, two MG 151/20 in the wing roots and two or four in a belly tray and two 30mm MK 108 firing upward at 65° in a Schräge Musik (Jazz Music) installation for destroying bombers by formating below them. The A-7/R1 had MK 108s in the wing roots and two of these big guns and two MG 151/20 in the tray, plus the Schräge Musik with 100 rounds per gun (the most lethal of all). Some versions had three seats, long-span wing and DB 603L turbocharged engines, or Jumo 213s or even the 2,500hp Jumo 222 with six banks of four cylinders. The B and C families would have been enlarged multi-role versions with rear turrets. Total A-type production was only 268, the officials at one time ignoring Luftwaffe enthusiasm by ordering production to be stopped!

The He 219A-7/R4 had exceptional high-altitude equipment and performance, plus ejection seats, but armament was reduced to four MG 151/20, all firing ahead. This was relatively light.

Above: An He 219A-5/R2 just after capture of its airfield by the Allies. Splendid to fly, the 219 was a formidable machine.

Below: Another He 219A-5, this time fitted with not only SN-2 radar but also the older Lichtenstein C-1 in the centre.

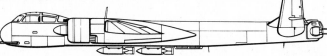

Above: The proposed He 219C-2 Jagdbomber with Jumo 222 engines.

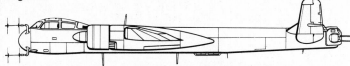

Above: The proposed He 219C-1 four-seat night fighter.

Henschel Hs 123

Hs 123A-1

Origin: Henschel Flugzeugwerke AG.
Type: Single-seat dive bomber and close-support.
Engine: One 880hp BMW 132 Dc nine-cylinder radial.
Dimensions: Span 34ft 5½in (10·5m); length 27ft 4in (8·3m) height 10ft 6½in (3·2m).
Weights: Empty 3,316lb (1504kg); loaded 4,888lb (2217kg).
Performance: Maximum speed 214mph (345km/h); initial climb 2,950ft (900m)/min; service ceiling 29,530 ft (9000m); range 530 miles (850km).
Armament: Two 7·92mm Rheinmetall MG 17 machine guns ahead of pilot; underwing racks for four 110lb (50kg) bombs, or clusters of anti-personnel bombs or two 20mm MG FF cannon.
History: First flight, spring 1935 (public display given 8 May); first delivery (Spain) December 1936; final delivery, October 1938.
User: Germany (Luftwaffe).

Development: Though representing a class of aircraft generally considered obsolete by the start of World War II, this trim little biplane was kept

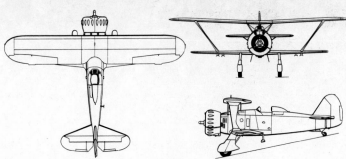

Above: Three-view of the Hs 123A-1.

hard at work until 1942, achieving results which in retrospect seem almost unbelievable. The prototype needed extensive modification to produce the A-1 production version, which was tested in the Spanish Civil War. Contrary to the staff-college theories then adhered to by the newly formed Luftwaffe, the Henschels were able to give close support to ground troops of a most real and immediate kind, strafing and bombing with great accuracy despite the lack of any radio link or even an established system of operation. Eventually the Luftwaffe realised that the concept of a close-support aircraft was valid. and a few Henschels were allowed to operate in this role, but all the effort and money was put into the Ju 87, and the Hs 123 was phased out of production before World War II. Yet in the Polish campaign these aircraft proved unbelievably useful, having the ability to make pinpoint attacks with guns and bombs and, by virtue of careful setting of the propeller speed, to make a demoralising noise. Moreover, it established an extraordinary reputation for returning to base even after direct hits by AA shells. As a result, though the whole force was incessantly threatened with disbandment or replacement by later types, the Hs 123 close-support unit II (Schlacht)/LG2 was sent intact to the Balkans in April 1941 and thence to the USSR. Here the old biplanes fought around the clock, proving far better adapted to the conditions than more modern types and continuing in front-line operations until, by the end of 1944, there were no more left.

Left: An Hs 123A-1 in front-line service, possibly with Schlacht/LG 2, in the campaign in France or the Balkans. By 1942 hardly any of the Henschels still wore their spats.

Henschel Hs 126

Hs 126A and B

Origin: Henschel Flugzeugwerke AG, Schönefeld.
Type: Army co-operation; later multi-role tactical.
Engine: One nine-cylinder radial, (A-O) 830hp Bramo Fafnir 323A, (A-1) 880hp BMW 132 Dc, (B) 900hp BMW Bramo Fafnir 323A-2 or Q-2.
Dimensions: Span 47ft 6¾in (14·50m); length 35ft 7¾in (10·85m); height 12ft 3¾in (3·75m).
Weights: Empty (B-1) 4,480lb (2032kg); maximum 7,209lb (3270kg).
Performance: Maximum speed 221mph (355km/h); service ceiling 27,070ft (8250m); maximum range at sea level 360 miles (580km).
Armament: One synchronized 7·92mm MG 17 and one manually aimed 7·92mm MG 15; light bombs or 110lb (50kg) bomb or extra tank.
History: First flight August 1936; service delivery (A-O) June 1937; final delivery January 1941.
Users: Bulgaria, Croatia, Greece, Germany, Spain.

Development: Developed in early 1936 from the disappointing Hs 122, the parasol-winged Hs 126 was a thoroughly sound machine very like the British Lysander in character though more conventional. The crew of two sat below and behind the wing in a capacious tandem cockpit, the pilot's portion being enclosed. Typical photographic, radio and light bombing equipment was carried, and the aircraft proved to have excellent STOL

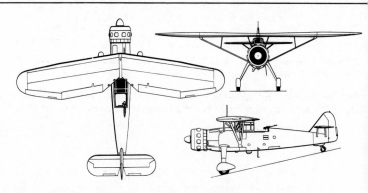

Above: Three-view of the Hs 126A (B-series, almost identical). By about 1941 nearly all the spats had been removed.

capability and ability to absorb much punishment. Altogether about 802 were delivered, maintaining the Aufklärungsstaffeln (recce squadrons) at a front-line strength of around 280 aircraft. By June 1941 virtually all were on the Eastern Front or in the Balkans or North Africa. A few survived until 1944—45 in operations against partisans in the Balkans, but most had been replaced by the Fw 189 and used for towing gliders. The 200-odd combat veterans served in Nachtschlacht (night ground attack) wings, often using a variety of armament schemes.

Left: This Hs 126A-1 was serving with 2.(H)/31 (Pz) from a base in Greece in April 1941. Like more than half the 126 strength, this machine was assigned to a Panzer corps, whose emblem it wears. Increasingly, the Fw 189 took over the front-line reconnaissance missions while the parasol-winged 126 was relegated to supply dropping, harrying partisans and general utility communications.

Henschel Hs 129

Hs 129A and B series

Origin: Henschel Flugzeugwerke AG.
Type: Single-seat close support and ground attack.
Engines: (B-series) two 690hp Gnome-Rhône 14M 04/05 14-cylinder two-row radials.
Dimensions: Span 46ft 7in (14·2m); length 31ft 11¾in (9·75m); height 10ft 8in (3·25m).
Weights: (Typical B-1) empty 8,940lb (4060kg); loaded 11,265lb (5110kg).
Performance: (Typical B-1) maximum speed 253mph (408km/h); initial climb 1,390ft (425m)/min; service ceiling 29,530ft (9000m); range 547 miles (880km).
Armament: See text.
History: First flight (Hs 129V-1) early 1939; service delivery (129A-0) early 1941; first flight (129B) October 1941; service delivery (129B) late 1942.
Users: Germany (Luftwaffe), Hungary, Romania.

Development: Though there were numerous types of specialised close support and ground attack aircraft in World War I, this category was virtually ignored until the Spanish Civil War showed, again, that it is one of the most

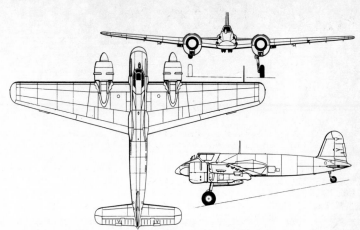

Above: Three-view of Hs 129B-1/R4 with bomb kit.

Above: A Henschel Hs 129B-2/R2 of Schlachtgeschwader 9 on the Eastern Front, spring 1943 but still in winter colours.

Below: Another Hs 129B-2, in this case of 4 (Pz)/Sch.G 1, from the same period, with 70/71 oversprayed with white blobs.

important of all. In 1938 the RLM issued a specification for such an aircraft — the whole purpose of the Luftwaffe being to support the Wehrmacht in Blitzkrieg-type battles — to back up the purpose-designed Ju 87 dive bomber. Henschel's Dipl-Ing F. Nicholaus designed a trim machine somewhat resembling the twin-engined fighters of the period but with more armour and less-powerful engines (two 495hp Argus As 410A-1 air-cooled inverted-vee-12s). The solo pilot sat in the extreme nose behind a windscreen 3in thick, with armour surrounding the cockpit. The triangular-section fuselage housed self-sealing tanks, guns in the sloping sides and a hardpoint for a bomb underneath. Test pilots at Rechlin damned the A-0 pre-production batch as grossly underpowered, but these aircraft were used on the Eastern Front by the Romanian Air Force. The redesigned B-series used the vast numbers of French 14M engines that were available and in production by the Vichy government for the Me 323. Altogether 841 B-series were built, and used with considerable effect on the Eastern Front but with less success in North Africa. The B-1/R1 had two 7·92mm MG 17 and two 20mm MG 151/20, plus two 110lb or 48 fragmentation bombs. The R2 had a 30mm MK 101 clipped underneath and was the first aircraft ever to use a 30mm gun in action. The R3 had a ventral box of four MG 17. The R4 carried up to 551lb of bombs. The R5 had a camera for vertical photography. The B-2 series changed the inbuilt MG 17s for MG 131s and other subtypes had many kinds of armament including the 37mm BK 3·7 and 75mm BK 7·5 with muzzle about eight feet ahead of the nose. The most novel armament, used against Russian armour with results that were often devastating, was a battery of six smooth-bore 75mm tubes firing recoilless shells down and to the rear with automatic triggering as the aircraft flew over metal objects.

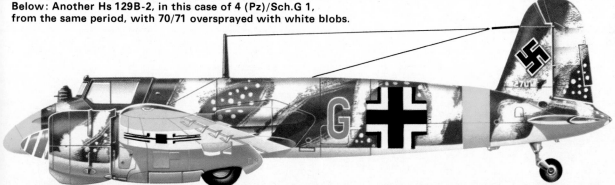

Below: A highly cleaned-up and somewhat falsified Hs 129B (sub-type obscured by changes including removal of the large pilot sight) in American charge long after World War II. Only two Hs 129s are thought to exist today.

Junkers Ju 52/3m

Ju 52/3m in many versions; data for 3mg5e to 3mg14e

Origin: Junkers Flugzeug und Motorenwerke AG; also built in France on German account by a SNCASO/Breguet/Amiot group; built under licence by CASA, Spain.

Type: Passenger and freight transport (also bomber, reconnaissance, mine countermeasures, cas-evac and glider tug).

Engines: Three (one in Ju 52) of following types: 600hp BMW Hornet, 725hp BMW 132A, 830hp BMW 132T (standard on nearly all wartime versions), 925hp Bristol or PZL Pegasus, 750hp ENMASA Beta E-9C or 710hp Wright Cyclone (all nine-cylinder radials) or Jumo 5 diesel, Jumo 206 or BMW VI in-lines.

Dimensions: Span 95ft 11½in (29·25m); length 62ft (18·9m); height (landplane) 14ft 9in (4·5m).

Weights: Empty 12,346lb (5600kg); loaded 24,317lb (11,030kg).

Performance: Maximum speed 190mph (305km/h); initial climb 689ft (210m)/min; service ceiling 18,045ft (5500m); range 808 miles (1300km).

Armament: Usually none; in combat zones it was usual to mount one 13mm MG 131 manually aimed from open dorsal cockpit and two 7·92mm MG 15s manually aimed from beam windows.

History: First flight (Ju 52) 13 October 1930; (Ju 52/3m) May 1932; (Ju 52/3mg3e bomber) October 1934; final delivery (AAC.1) August 1947; (CASA 352-L) 1952.

Users: Argentina, Colombia, Ecuador, France, Germany (Luftwaffe, Kriegsmarine, Lufthansa), Hungary, Peru, Portugal, Slovakia, Spain, Sweden.

Development: One of the great aircraft of history, the Ju 52/3m was briefly preceded by the single-engined Ju 52 which had no military history. Most early Ju 52/3m versions were 15/17-passenger airliners which sold all over the world and also made up 75 per cent of the giant fleet of Lufthansa (reducing that airline's forced landings per million kilometres from 7 to only

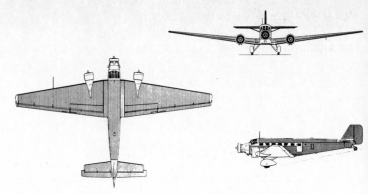

Above: Three-view of typical pre-war civil Ju 52/3m.

1·5). In 1935 the 3mg3e bomber, with manually aimed MG 15s in a dorsal cockpit and ventral dustbin and bomb load of 3,307lb (1500kg) equipped the first bomber squadrons of the Luftwaffe. By 1936 about half the 450 built had been supplied to the Legion Kondor in Spain and to the Nationalist air force, but nearly all were equipped as troop transports, freighters and casualty-evacuation ambulances. These were the roles of most military versions, which were by far the most common transports on every front on which Nazi Germany fought. It is typical of the Nazi regime that, despite a wealth of later and more capable aircraft, the old "Auntie Ju" or "Iron Annie" was kept in full production throughout the war. Good STOL performance, with patented "double wing" flaps, robust construction, interchangeable wheel/ski/float landing gear and great reliability were the Ju 52's attributes. Total German output was 4,845. Many were built in France where 400 were completed as AAC.1s in 1947. The final 170 were built in Spain as CASA 352-Ls for the Spanish Air Force, which used them as T.2B multi-role transports until 1975.

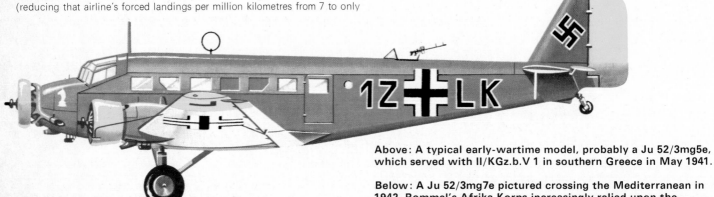

Above: A typical early-wartime model, probably a Ju 52/3mg5e, which served with II/KGz.b.V 1 in southern Greece in May 1941.

Below: A Ju 52/3mg7e pictured crossing the Mediterranean in 1942. Rommel's Afrika Korps increasingly relied upon the "Tante Ju" (Auntie Ju), which suffered high attrition.

Junkers Ju 86

Ju 86D, E, G, K, P and R

Origin: Junkers Flugzeug und Motorenwerke AG; also built by Henschel, and built under licence by Saab, Sweden.

Type: (D, E, G and K) bomber; (P) bomber/reconnaissance; (R) reconnaissance.

Engines: (D) two 600hp Junkers Jumo 205C six opposed-piston cylinder diesels; (E, G) two 800 or 880hp BMW 132 nine-cylinder radials; (K) two 905hp Bristol Mercury XIX nine-cylinder radials; (P, R) two 1,000hp Jumo 207A-1 or 207B-3/V turbocharged opposed-piston diesels.

Dimensions: Span 73ft 10in (22·6m); (P) 84ft (25·6m); (R) 105ft (32m); length (typical) 58ft 8½in (17·9m); (G) 56ft 5in; (P, R) 54ft; height (all) 15ft 5in (4·7m).

Weights: Empty (E-1) 11,464lb (5200kg); (R-1) 14,771lb (6700kg); loaded (E-1) 18,080lb (8200kg); (R-1) 25,420lb (11,530kg).

Performance: Maximum speed (E-1) 202mph (325km/h); (R-1) 261mph (420km/h); initial climb (E) 918ft (280m)/min; service ceiling (E-1) 22,310ft (6800m); (R-1) 42,650ft (13,000m); range (E) 746 miles (1200km); (R-1) 980 miles (1577km).

Armament: (D, E, G, K) three 7·92mm MG 15 manually aimed from nose, dorsal and retractable ventral positions; internal bomb load of four 551lb (250kg) or 16 110lb (50kg) bombs; (P) single 7·92mm fixed MG 17, same bomb load; (R) usually none.

History: First flight (Ju 86V-1) 4 November 1934; (V-5 bomber prototype) January 1936; (production D-1) late 1936; (P-series prototype) February 1940.

Users: Bolivia, Chile, Germany (Luftwaffe, Lufthansa), Hungary, Portugal, South Africa, Spain, Sweden.

Development: Planned like the He 111 as both a civil airliner and a bomber, the Ju 86 was in 1934 one of the most advanced aircraft in Europe. The design team under Dipl-Ing Zindel finally abandoned corrugated skin and created a smooth and efficient machine with prominent double-wing flaps and outward-retracting main gears. The diesel-engined D-1 was quickly put into Luftwaffe service to replace the Do 23 and Ju 52 as the standard heavy bomber, but in Spain the various D-versions proved

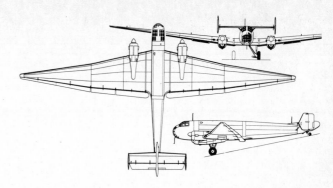

Above: Three-view of the ultimate extreme-altitude Ju 86, the Ju 86R-1. Their chief accomplishment was to trigger the development of numerous Allied high-altitude fighters.

vulnerable even to biplane fighters. The E-series bombers, with the powerful BMW radial, were faster and the fastest of all were the Swedish Bristol-engined Ks, of which 40 were built by Junkers (first delivery 18 December 1936) and 16 by Saab (last delivery 3 January 1941). Many D and E bombers were used against Poland, but that was their swan-song. By 1939 Junkers was working on a high-altitude version with turbocharged engines and a pressure cabin and this emerged as the P-1 bomber and P-2 bomber/reconnaissance which was operational over the Soviet Union gathering pictures before the German invasion of June 1941. The R series had a span increased even beyond that of the P and frequently operated over southern England in 1941–2 until – with extreme difficulty – solitary Spitfires managed to reach their altitude and effect an interception. Total military Ju 86 production was between 810 and 1,000. Junkers schemed many developed versions, some having four or six engines.

Below: One of the colourful Ju 86K-2 bombers of the Hungarian 3./I Bombázó Oszataly, based at Tapolca in 1938. Few were left when the Axis attacked the Soviet Union in 1941.

Below: The Ju 86G-1 was the only sub-type still in combat service with the Luftwaffe at the start of the Polish campaign in 1939.

Junkers Ju 87

Ju 87A, B and D series

Origin: Junkers Flugzeug und Motorenwerke AG; also built by Weser Flugzeugbau and SNCASO, France.
Type: Two-seat dive bomber and ground attack.

Below: The cutaway drawing shows the Ju 87D-3, one of the more powerful and aerodynamically improved D-series that made up more than three-quarters of all production. The bombs shown, with Dienartstab fuzes, are among a great diversity of weapons and equipment that could be carried.

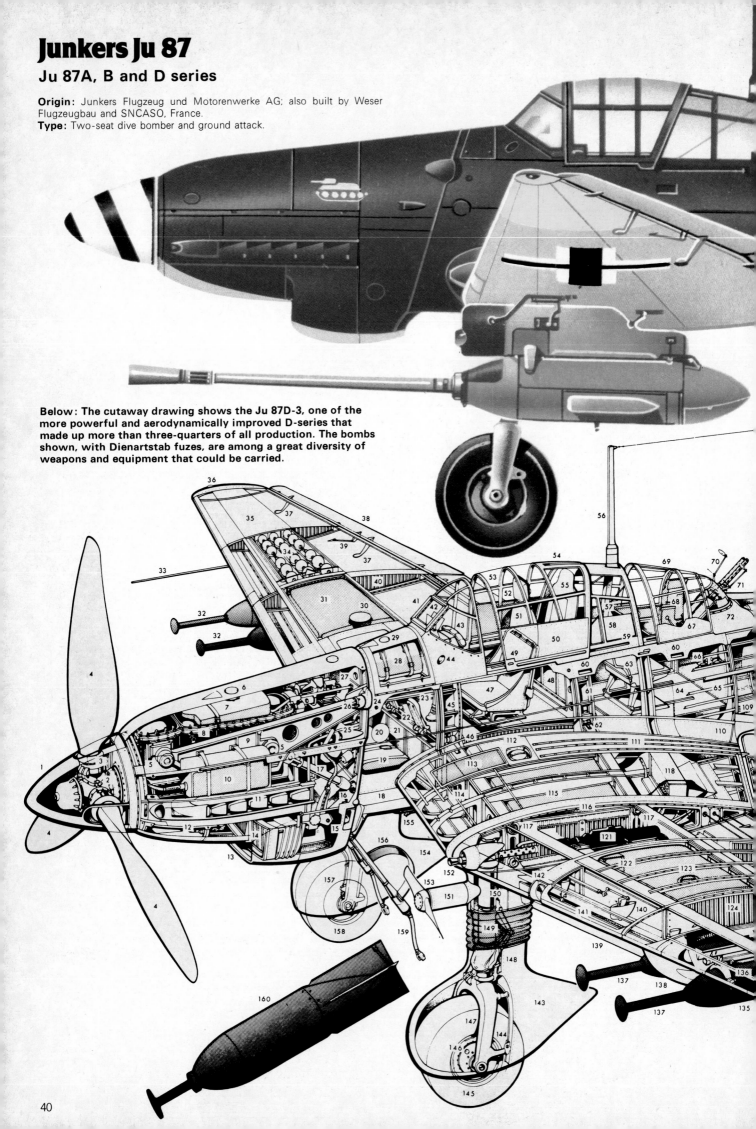

Below: Though the futility of using ordinary bombs against tanks was recognised on the fourth day of the German invasion of the Soviet Union, it was not until 1943 that a better answer became available. This Ju 87G-1 was probably serving with 10 (Pz)/SG 2 on the Eastern Front in October 1943.

Junkers Ju 87D-3 cutaway drawing key:

1 Spinner
2 Pitch change mechanism housing
3 Blade hub
4 Junkers VS 11 constant-speed propeller
5 Anti-vibration engine mounting attachments
6 Oil filler point and marker
7 Auxiliary oil tank (5·9 Imp gal./26·8l capacity)
8 Junkers Jumo 211J-1 12-cylinder inverted-vee liquid cooled engine
9 Magnesium alloy forged engine mount
10 Coolant (Glysantin-water) header tank
11 Ejector exhaust stubs
12 Fuel injection unit housing
13 Induction air cooler
14 Armoured radiator
15 Inertia starter cranking point
16 Ball joint bulkhead fixing (lower)
17 Tubular steel mount support strut
18 Ventral armour (8mm)
19 Main oil tank (9·9 Imp gal (45l capacity)
20 Oil filling point
21 Transverse support frame
22 Rudder pedals
23 Control column
24 Heating point
25 Auxiliary air intake
26 Ball joint bulkhead fixing (upper)
27 Bulkhead
28 Oil tank (6·8 Imp gal/31l capacity)
29 Oil filler point and marker (Intava 100)
30 Fuel filler cap
31 Self-sealing starboard outer fuel tank (33 Imp gal/150l capacity)
32 Underwing bombs with *Dienartstab* percussion rods
33 Pitot head
34 Spherical oxygen bottles
35 Wing skinning
36 Starboard navigation light
37 Aileron mass balance
38 'Double wing' aileron and flap (starboard outer)
39 Aileron hinge
40 Corrugated wing rib station
41 Reinforced armoured windscreen
42 Reflector sight
43 Padded crash bar
44 Signal flare tube
45 Braced fuselage mainframe
46 Front spar/fuselage attachment point
47 Pilot's seat (reinforced with 4-mm side and 8-mm rear armour)
48 Inter-cockpit bulkhead
49 Sliding canopy handgrip
50 External side armour
51 Pilot's back armour (8mm)
52 Headrest
53 Aft-sliding cockpit canopy (shown part open)
54 Radio mast cut-out
55 Anti-crash hoop (magnesium casting)
56 Radio mast
57 Radio equipment (FuGe 16) compartment
58 Additional (internal) side armour
59 Canopy track
60 Handhold/footrests
61 Braced fuselage mainframe
62 Rear spar/fuselage attachment point
63 Radio-operator/gunner's seat (folding)
64 Floor armour (5mm)
65 Armoured bulkhead (8mm)
66 Ammunition magazine racks
67 Additional (external) side armour with cut-out for hand grip
68 Internal side and head armour
69 Sliding canopy section (shown part open)
70 Ring-and-bead gunsights
71 Twin 7·9-mm Mauser MG 81Z machine gun on GSL-K 81 mount
72 Canopy track fairing
73 Peil G IV D/F equipment
74 Circular plexiglass access panel
75 Back-to-back L-section stringers (fuselage horizontal break)
76 First-aid stowage
77 Z-section fuselage frames
78 Radio aerial
79 Faired elevator mass balance
80 Starboard elevator
81 Tailplane structure
82 Tailplane brace/spar attachment point
83 Tailplane bracing strut
84 Fuselage skinning
85 Control runs
86 Tailfin attachment fairing
87 Tailfin structure
88 Rudder horn balance
89 Rudder
90 Rudder trim tab controls
91 Rudder trim tab
92 Rudder control linkage
93 Rudder post
94 Rear navigation light
95 Elevator tab
96 Port elevator
97 Faired elevator mass balance
98 Tailplane front spar
99 Control pulley circular access panels
100 Rudder lower hinge fairing
101 Tailplane bracing strut
102 Emergency tailskid
103 Tailwheel
104 Tailwheel leg
105 Jacking point
106 Fuselage stringers
107 Master compass
108 Crew entry step (port and starboard)
109 Entry step support (with control run cut-outs)
110 Wing root fairing
111 Non-slip walkway (aft section external metal strakes)
112 Fuel filler point
113 Non-slip walkway (forward section composite surface)
114 Leading-edge structure
115 Self-sealing port inner wing fuel tank (52·8 Imp gal/240l capacity)
116 Wing-joint external cover strip
117 Ball-and-socket wing attachment points
118 Armoured coolant radiator (port and starboard)
119 Inboard flap structure
120 Flap hinge
121 Rheinmetall-Borsig MG 17 machine gun of 7·92-mm calibre (port and starboard)
122 Ammunition tank (1,000 rounds capacity) inboard of rib
123 Port outer self-sealing fuel tank (33 Imp gal/150l capacity)
124 Corrugated wing rib
125 ETC bomb rack support bar
126 ETC bomb rack underwing fairing
127 Port outboard flap
128 Port aileron
129 Aileron mass balance
130 Rear spar
131 Wing rib
132 Port navigation light
133 Front spar
134 Wing leading edge
135 Underwing bomb load (two 110-lb/50-kg bombs) on multi-purpose carrier
136 Bomb shackles
137 *Dienartstab* percussion rod attachments
138 ETC 50/VIII fairing
139 Air brake (extended)
140 Air brake activating mechanism
141 Air brake (retracted)
142 Landing lamp
143 Wheel spat
144 Fork/spat attachment
145 Port mainwheel
146 Brake reservoir filler point
147 Cantilever fork
148 Leather shroud
149 Oleo-pneumatic shock absorber
150 Mainwheel leg
151 Siren fairing
152 Barrel of MG 17 machine gun
153 Wind-driven siren
154 Starboard wheel spat
155 PVC ventral bomb rack
156 Bomb cradle
157 Starboard wheel fork
158 Starboard mainwheel
159 Bomb release trapese
160 551-lb (250-kg) bomb with *Dienartstab* attachment

Above: This Ju 87R is seen in Norway in April 1940. Then a new model, it carried extra fuel plus underwing tanks.

41

Engine: (Ju 87B-1) one 1,100hp Junkers Jumo 211Da 12-cylinder inverted-vee liquid-cooled; (Ju 87D-1, D-5) 1,300hp Jumo 211J.

Dimensions: Span (Ju 87B-1, D-1) 45ft 3¼in (13·8m); (D-5) 50ft 0½in (15·25m); length 36ft 5in (11·1m); height 12ft 9in (3·9m).

Weights: Empty (B-1, D-1) about 6,080lb (2750kg); loaded (B-1) 9,371lb (4250kg); (D-1) 12,600lb (5720kg); (D-5) 14,500lb (6585kg).

Performance: Maximum speed (B-1) 242mph (390km/h); (D-1) 255mph (408km/h); (D-5) 250mph (402km/h); service ceiling (B-1) 26,250ft (8000m); (D-1, D-5) 24,000ft (7320m); range with maximum bomb load (B-1) 373 miles (600km); (D-1, D-5) 620 miles (1000km).

Armament: (Ju 87B-1) two 7·92mm Rheinmetall MG 17 machine guns in wings, one 7·92mm MG 15 manually aimed in rear cockpit, one 1,102lb (500kg) bomb on centreline and four 110lb (50kg) on wing racks; (D-1, D-5) two MG 17 in wings, twin 7·92mm MG 81 machine guns manually aimed in rear cockpit, one bomb of 3,968lb (1800kg) on centreline; (D-7) two 20mm MG 151/20 cannon in wings; (Ju 87G-1) two 37mm BK (Flak 18, or Flak 36) cannon in underwing pods; (D-4) two underwing WB81 weapon containers each housing six MG 81 guns.

History: First flight (Ju 87V1) late 1935; (pre-production Ju 87A-0) November 1936; (Ju 87B-1) August 1938; (Ju 87D-1) 1940; termination of production 1944.

Users: Bulgaria, Croatia, Germany (Luftwaffe), Hungary, Italy, Romania, Slovakia.

Development: Until at least 1942 the Ju 87 "Stuka" enjoyed a reputation that struck terror into those on the ground beneath it. First flown with a British R-R Kestrel engine and twin fins in 1935, it entered production in 1937 as the Ju 87A with large trousered landing gear and full equipment for dive bombing, including a heavy bomb crutch that swung the missile well clear of the fuselage before release. The spatted Ju 87B was the first aircraft in production with the Jumo 211 engine, almost twice as powerful as the Jumo 210 of the Ju 87A, and it had an automatic device (almost an auto-pilot) to ensure proper pull-out from the steep dive, as well as red lines at 60°, 75° and 80° painted on the pilot's side window. Experience in Spain had shown that pilots could black-out and lose control in the pull-out. Later a whole formation of Ju 87Bs in Spain was late pulling out over misty ground

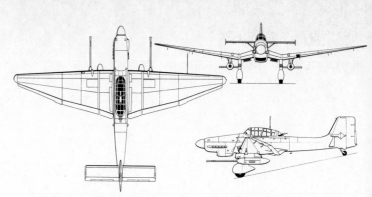

Above: The Ju 87G-1 anti-tank aircraft with two 37mm guns.

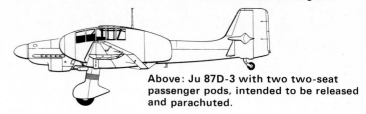

Above: Ju 87D-3 with two two-seat passenger pods, intended to be released and parachuted.

and many hit the ground. In Poland and the Low Countries the Ju 87 was terribly effective and it repeated its success in Greece, Crete and parts of the Russian front. But in the Battle of Britain its casualty rate was such that it was soon withdrawn, thereafter to attack ships and troops in areas where the Axis still enjoyed some air superiority. In 1942–45 its main work was close support on the Eastern front, attacking armour with big guns (Ju 87G-1) and even being used as a transport and glider tug. Total production, all by Junkers, is believed to have been 5,709.

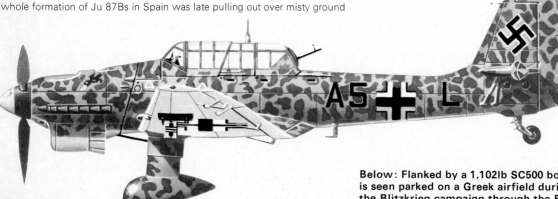

Left: A Ju 87B-2/Trop serving with III/StG 1 in Libya in 1941. The equipment of StG 1 had mostly been in action in Poland and the Low Countries, France and England since the start of the war.

Below: Flanked by a 1,102lb SC500 bomb, this Ju 87B "Stuka" is seen parked on a Greek airfield during the continuation of the Blitzkrieg campaign through the Balkans into north Africa. This was the last campaign in which the Ju 87 demolished its targets and encountered little opposition.

Junkers Ju 88

Many versions: data for Ju 88A-4, C-6, G-7, S-1

Origin: Junkers Flugzeug und Motorenwerke AG, dispersed among 14 plants with subcontract or assembly by ATG, Opel, Volkswagen and various French groups.

Type: Military aircraft designed as dive bomber but developed for level bombing, close support, night fighting, torpedo dropping, reconnaissance and as pilotless missile. Crew: two to six.

Engines: (A-4) two 1,340hp Junkers Jumo 211J 12-cylinder inverted-vee liquid-cooled; (C-6) same as A-4; (G-7) two 1,880hp Junkers Jumo 213E 12-cylinder inverted-vee liquid-cooled; (S-1) two 1,700hp BMW 801G 18-cylinder two-row radials.

Dimensions: Span 65ft 10½in (20·13m) (early versions 59ft 10¾in); length 47ft 2¼in (14·4m); (G-7, 54ft 1½in); height 15ft 11in (4·85m); (C-6) 16ft 7½in (5m).

Weights: Empty (A-4) 17,637lb (8000kg); (C-6b) 19,090lb (8660kg), (G-7b) 20,062lb (9100kg); (S-1) 18,300lb (8300kg); maximum loaded (A-4) 30,865lb (14,000kg); (C-6b) 27,500lb (12,485kg); (G-7b) 32,350lb (14,690kg); (S-1) 23,100lb (10,490kg).

Performance: Maximum speed (A-4) 269mph (433km/h); (C-6b) 300mph (480km/h); (G-7b) (no drop tank or flame-dampers) 402mph (643km/h); (S-1) 373mph (600km/h); initial climb (A-4) 1,312ft (400m)/min; (C-6b) about 985ft (300m)/min; (G-7b) 1,640ft (500m)/min; (S-1) 1,804ft (550m)/min; service ceiling (A-4) 26,900ft (8200m); (C-6b) 32,480ft (9900m); (G-7b) 28,870ft (8800m); (S-1) 36,090ft (11,000m); range (A-4) 1,112 miles (1790km); (C-6b) 1,243 miles (2000km); (G-7b) 1,430 miles (2300km); (S-1) 1,243 miles (2000km).

Armament: (A-4) two 7.92mm MG 81 (or one MG 81 and one 13mm MG 131) firing forward, twin MG 81 or one MG 131 upper rear, one or two MG 81 at rear of ventral gondola and (later aircraft) two MG 81 at front of gondola; (C-6b) three 20mm MG FF and three MG 17 in nose and two 20mm MG 151/20 firing obliquely upward in Schräge Musik installation; (G-7b) four MG 151/20 (200 rounds each) firing forward from ventral fairing, two MG 151/20 in Schräge Musik installation (200 rounds each) and defensive MG 131 (500 rounds) swivelling in rear roof; (S-1) one MG 131 (500 rounds) swivelling in rear roof; bomb loads (A-4) 1,100lb (500kg) internal and four external racks rated at 2,200lb (1000kg) (inners) and 1,100lb (500kg) (outers) to maximum total bomb load of 6,614lb (3000kg); (C-6b and G-7b, nil); (S-1) up to 4,410lb (2000kg) on external racks.

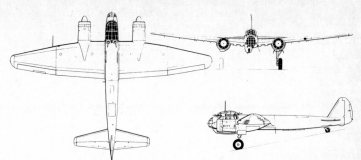

Above: Three-view of the first long-span version, the A-4.

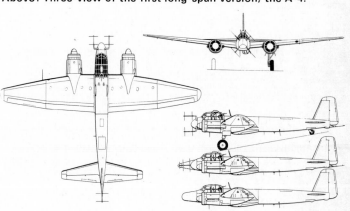

Above: Three-view of the Ju 88G-7a night fighter, with side elevations of G-7b (centre, FuG 218 Neptun) and -7c (FuG 240).

History: First flight (Ju 88V1) 21 December 1936; (first Ju 88A-1) 7 September 1939; (first fighter, Ju 88C-0) July 1939; (Ju 88C-6) mid-1942; (first G-series) early 1944; (S series) late 1943; final deliveries, only as factories were overrun by Allies.

Users: Bulgaria (briefly), Finland, Germany (Luftwaffe), Hungary, Italy, Romania.

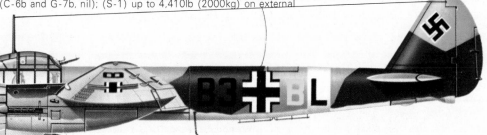

Left: Ju 88A-4 of I/KG 54 "Totenkopf" (Death's Head) at Gerbini, April 1942; colours 78/79/80.

Below: Yet another A-4, this time belonging to one of the most famous units, I/KG 51 "Edelweiss". It was photographed on the Eastern Front in the summer of 1941, in 70/71/65 trim.

Development: Probably no other aircraft in history has been developed in so many quite different forms for so many purposes – except, perhaps, for the Mosquito. Flown long before World War II as a civil prototype, after a rapid design process led by two temporarily hired Americans well-versed in modern stressed-skin construction, the first 88s were transformed into the heavier, slower and more capacious A-1 bombers which were just entering service as World War II began. The formidable bomb load and generally good performance were offset by inadequate defensive armament, and in the A-4 the span was increased, the bomb load and gun power substantially augmented and a basis laid for diverse further development. Though it would be fair to describe practically all the subsequent versions as a hodge-podge of lash-ups, the Ju 88 was structurally excellent, combined large internal fuel capacity with great load-carrying capability, and yet was never so degraded in performance as to become seriously vulnerable as were the Dornier and Heinkel bombers. Indeed, with the BMW radial and the Jumo 213 engines the later versions were almost as fast as the best contemporary fighters at all altitudes and could be aerobatted violently into the bargain. A basic design feature was that all the crew were huddled together, to improve combat morale; but in the Battle of Britain it was found this merely made it difficult to add proper defensive armament and in the later Ju 188 a much larger crew compartment was provided. Another distinctive feature was the large single struts of the main landing gear, sprung with stacks of chamfered rings of springy steel, and arranged to turn the big, soft-field wheels through 90° to lie flat in the rear of the nacelles. In 1940 to 1943 about 2,000 Ju 88 bombers were built each year, nearly all A-5 or A-4 versions. After splitting off completely new branches which led to the Ju 188 and 388, bomber development was directed to the streamlined S series of much higher performance, it having become accepted that the traditional Luftwaffe species of bomber was doomed if intercepted, no matter how many extra guns and crew it might carry. Indeed even the bomb and fuel loads were cut in most S sub-types, though the S-2 had fuel in the original bomb bay and large bulged bomb stowage (which defeated the objective of reducing drag). Final bomber versions included the P series of big-gun anti-armour and close-support machines, the Nbwe with flame-throwers and recoilless rocket projectors, and a large family of Mistel composite-aircraft combinations, in which the Ju 88 lower portion was a pilotless missile steered by the fighter originally mounted on top. Altogether bomber, reconnaissance and related 88s totalled 10,774, while frantic construction of night fighter versions in 1944–45 brought the total to at least 14,980. The Ju 88 night fighters (especially the properly designed G-series) were extremely formidable, bristling with radar and weapons and being responsible for destroying more Allied night bombers than all other fighters combined.

Above: One of the first Ju 88 combat missions starts engines: a long-span A-5 model, with yellow-staffel spinners and two SC 250 bombs hung externally.

Below: One of countless Ju 88 lash-ups was the P-1 anti-tank heavy-gun platform with 75mm PaK 40 with large muzzle brake.

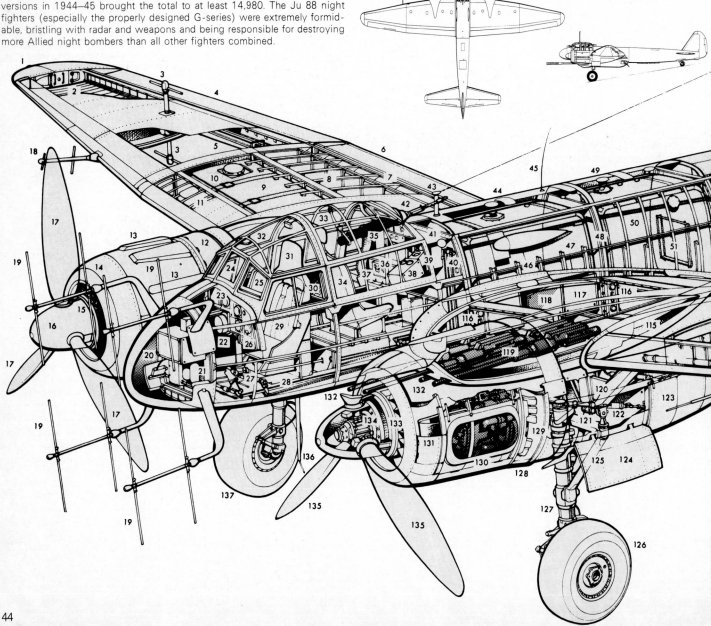

Above: One of the outstanding Ju 88 night fighters, the G-7a with Jumo 213 engines, Lichtenstein SN-2 FuG 220 radar and devastating armament.

Above: Another propaganda film shot of an early raid by a Ju 88A-5. Though still troublesome in 1939-40, the Ju 88 was the best German offensive aircraft.

Left: This cutaway reveals most of the salient features of the Ju 88G-1, the first of the purpose-designed night fighter versions with new Ju 188-type tail and completely revised armament. No other night fighter in wide use in World War II carried so many effective sensors; but the RAF played into the enemy's hands by emitting streams of signals.

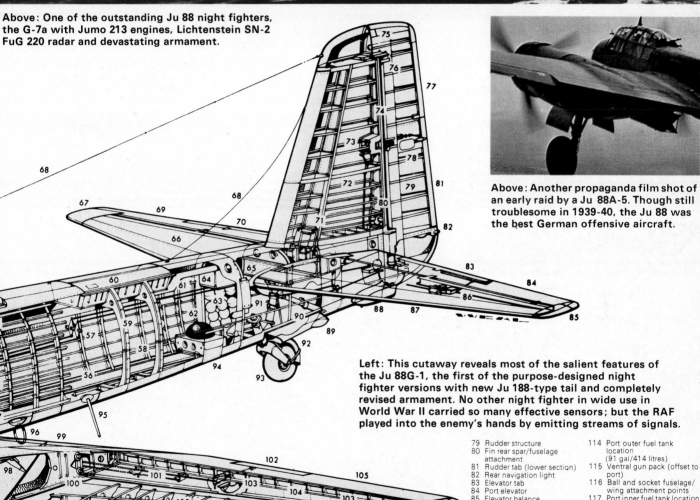

Junkers Ju 88G-1 cutaway drawing key:

1. Starboard navigation light
2. Wingtip profile
3. FuG 227 Flensburg homing receiver aerial
4. Starboard aileron
5. Aileron control lines
6. Starboard flap
7. Flap-fairing strip
8. Wing ribs
9. Starboard outer fuel tank (91 gal/414 litres)
10. Fuel filler cap
11. Leading-edge structure
12. Annular exhaust slot
13. Cylinder head fairings
14. Adjustable nacelle nose ring
15. Twelve-blade cooling fan
16. Propeller boss
17. Three-blade variable-pitch VS 111 propeller
18. Leading-edge radar array
19. Lichtenstein SN-2 radar array
20. SN-2 radar
21. Bulkhead
22. Gyro compass
23. Instrument panel
24. Armoured-glass windscreen sections
25. Folding seat
26. Control column
27. Rudder pedal/brake cylinder
28. Control lines
29. Pilot's seat
30. Sliding window section
31. Headrest
32. Jettisonable canopy roof section
33. Gun restraint
34. Radio operator/gunner's seat
35. 13mm MG 131 gun
36. Radio equipment
37. Ammunition box (500 rounds)
38. Lichtenstein SN-2 indicator box
39. FuG 227 Flensburg indicator box
40. Control linkage
41. Bulkhead
42. Armoured gun mounting
43. Aerial post/traverse check
44. Fuel filler cap
45. Whip aerial
46. Forward fuselage fuel tank (105 gal/480 litres)
47. Fuselage horizontal construction joint
48. Bulkhead
49. Fuel filler cap
50. Aft fuselage fuel tank (230 gal/1,046 litres)
51. Access hatch
52. Bulkhead
53. Control linkage access plate
54. Fuselage stringers
55. Upper longeron
56. Maintenance walkway
57. Control linkage
58. Fuselage horizontal construction joint
59. 'Z'-section fuselage frames
60. Dinghy stowage
61. Fuel vent pipe
62. Master compass
63. Spherical oxygen bottles
64. Accumulator
65. Tailplane centre-section carry-through
66. Starboard tailplane
67. Elevator balance
68. Aerial
69. Starboard elevator
70. Elevator tab
71. Fin front spar/fuselage attachment
72. Fin structure
73. Rudder actuator
74. Rudder post
75. Rudder mass balance
76. Rudder upper hinge
77. Rudder tab (upper section)
78. Inspection/maintenance handhold
79. Rudder structure
80. Fin rear spar/fuselage attachment
81. Rudder tab (lower section)
82. Rear navigation light
83. Elevator tab
84. Port elevator
85. Elevator balance
86. Elevator tab actuator
87. Heated leading-edge
88. Tailbumper/fuel vent outlet
89. Tailwheel doors
90. Tailwheel retraction mechanism
91. Shock-absorber leg
92. Mudgard
93. Tailwheel
94. Access hatch
95. Fixed antenna
96. D/F loop
97. Lower longeron
98. Nacelle/flap fairing
99. Port flap
100. Wing centre/outer section attachment point
101. Aileron controls
102. Aileron tab (port only)
103. Aileron hinges
104. Rear spar
105. Port aileron
106. Port navigation light
107. FuG 101a radio altimeter aerial
108. Wing structure
109. Leading-edge radar array
110. Front spar
111. Pitot head
112. Landing lamp
113. Mainwheel well rear bulkhead
114. Port outer fuel tank location (91 gal/414 litres)
115. Ventral gun pack (offset to port)
116. Ball and socket fuselage/wing attachment points
117. Port inner fuel tank location (93.4 gal/425 litres)
118. Ammunition boxes (200 rpg)
119. Four Mauser MG 151 20mm cannon
120. Mainwheel leg retraction yoke
121. Leg pivot member
122. Mainwheel door actuating jack
123. Mainwheel door (rear section)
124. Mainwheel door (front section)
125. Leg support strut
126. Port mainwheel
127. Mainwheel leg
128. Annular exhaust slot
129. Exhaust stubs (internal)
130. BMW 801D engine (part-deleted to show gun pack)
131. Annular oil tank
132. Cannon muzzles (5 deg. downward angle)
133. Twelve-blade cooling fan (3.17 times propeller speed)
134. Propeller mechanism
135. Three-blade variable-pitch VS 111 propeller
136. FuG 16ZY aerial
137. Starboard mainwheel

45

Junkers Ju 188

Ju 188A, D and E series, and Ju 388, J, K and L

Origin: Junkers Flugzeug und Motorenwerke AG; with subcontract manufacture of parts by various French companies.
Type: Five-seat bomber (D-2, reconnaissance).
Engines: (Ju 188A) two 1,776hp Junkers Jumo 213A 12-cylinder inverted-vee liquid-cooled; (Ju 188D) same as A; (Ju 188E) two 1,700hp BMW 801G-2 18-cylinder two-row radials.
Dimensions: Span 72ft 2in (22m); length 49ft 1in (14·96m); height 16ft 1in (4·9m).
Weights: Empty (188E-1) 21,825lb (9900kg); loaded (188A and D) 33,730lb (15,300kg); (188E-1) 31,967lb (14,500kg).
Performance: Maximum speed (188A) 325mph (420km/h) at 20,500ft (6250m); (188D) 350mph (560km/h) at 27,000ft (8235m); (188E) 315mph (494km/h) at 19,685ft (6000m); service ceiling (188A) 33,000ft (10,060m); (188D) 36,090ft (11,000m); (188E) 31,170ft (9500m); range with 3,300lb (1500kg) bomb load (188A and E) 1,550 miles (2480km).
Armament: (A, D-1 and E-1) one 20mm MG 151/20 cannon in nose, one MG 151/20 in dorsal turret, one 13mm MG 131 manually aimed at rear dorsal position and one MG 131 or twin 7·92mm MG 81 manually aimed at rear ventral position; 6,614lb (3000kg) bombs internally or two 2,200lb (1000kg) torpedoes under inner wings.
History: First flight (Ju 88B-0) early 1940; (Ju 88V27) September 1941; (Ju 188V1) December 1941; (Ju 188E-1) March 1942; (Ju 388L) May 1944.
User: Germany (Luftwaffe).

Development: In 1939 Junkers had the Jumo 213 engine in advanced development and, to go with it, the aircraft side of the company prepared an

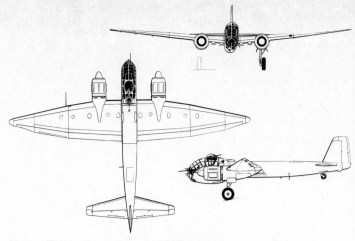

Above: Three-view of the Ju 188E-1 bomber, one of the versions with the BMW 801G-2 radial engine.

Below: Almost gaudy in 72/73 green shades oversprayed with 65 Light Blue, this Ju 188D-2 was operated by 1(F)/124 at Kirkenes, northern Norway, in 1944.

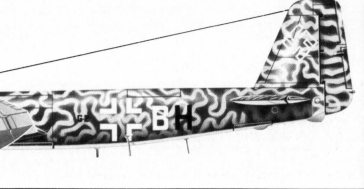

Junkers Ju 290

Ju 290A-1 to A-8 and B-1, B-2 and C

Origin: Junkers Flugzeug und Motorenwerke; design and development at Prague-Letnany, prototypes at Dessau and production at Bernberg.
Type: Long-range transport and reconnaissance bomber.
Engines: Four BMW 801 14-cylinder radials, (A) usually 1,700hp 801D, (B) 1,970hp 801E.
Dimensions: Span 137ft 9½in (42·00m); length 92ft 1in to 97ft 9in (A-5, 93ft 11½in, 28·64m); height 22ft 4¾in (6·83m).
Weights: Empty, not known (published figures cannot be correct); maximum (A-5) 99,141lb (44,970kg), (A-7) 101,413lb (45,400kg), (B-2) 111,332lb (50,500kg).
Performance: Maximum speed (all, without missiles) about 273mph (440km/h); maximum range (typical) 3,700 miles (5950km), (B-2) 4,970 miles (8000km).
Armament: See text.
History: First flight (rebuilt Ju 90V5) early 1939, (production 290A-0) October 1942; programme termination October 1944.
User: Germany (Luftwaffe).

Development: In 1936 Junkers considered the possibility of turning the Ju 89 strategic bomber into the Ju 90 airliner. With the death of Gen Wever the Ju 89 was cancelled and the Ju 90 became the pride of Deutsche Lufthansa. By 1937 the civil Ju 90S (Schwer = heavy) was in final design, with the powerful BMW 139 engine. By 1939 this had flown, with a new wing and BMW 801 engines, and via a string of development prototypes led to the Ju 290A-0 and A-1 transports first used at Stalingrad. The A-2 was an Atlantic patrol machine, with typical armament of five 20mm MG 151 (including two power turrets) and six 13mm MG 131. There were many other versions, and the A-7 introduced a bulbous glazed nose; armament of the A-8 series was ten MG 151 and one (or three) MG 131, the most powerful carried by any bomber of World War II. The B carried more fuel and pressurized crew compartments, and like some A versions had radar and could launch Hs 293 and other air/surface missiles. In 1944 three A-5 made round trips to Manchuria.

Right: Taken at the Junkers plant at Bernburg, the centre for Ju 290 development, this shows the first production A-7 (Werk-Nr 0186) being readied for flight in May 1944. The A-7 was the most advanced sub-type to reach production status; even so the initial batch of 25 was not completed.

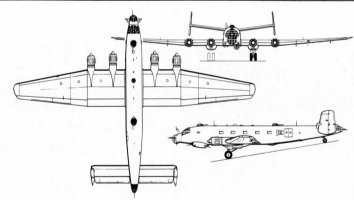

Above: One of the later sub-types was the Ju 290A-7, one of which is illustrated at the foot of the page.

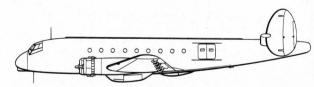

Above: The Ju 90 V4, a development aircraft of 1937 (pre-290).

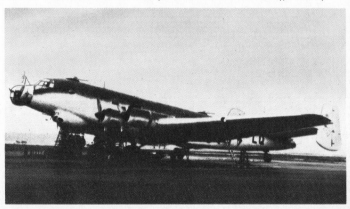

improved Ju 88 with a larger yet more streamlined crew compartment, more efficient pointed wings and large squarish tail. After protracted development this went into production as the Ju 188E-1, fitted with BMW 801s because the powerful Jumo was still not ready. The plant at Bernburg delivered 120 E-1s and a few radar-equipped turretless E-2s and reconnaissance F versions before, in mid-1943, finally getting into production with the A-1 version. Leipzig/Mockau built the A-2 with flame-damped exhaust for night operations and the A-3 torpedo bomber. The D was a fast reconnaissance aircraft, and the Ju 188S was a family of high-speed machines, for various duties, capable of up to 435mph (696km/h). Numerous other versions, some with a remotely controlled twin-MG 131 tail turret, led to the even faster and higher-flying Ju 388 family of night fighters (J), reconnaissance (L) and bomber aircraft (K). Altogether about 1,100 Ju 188 and about 120 388s were delivered, while at the war's end the much larger and markedly different Ju 288 had been shelved and the Ju 488, a much enlarged four-engined 388, had been built at Toulouse. All these aircraft, and the even greater number of stillborn projects, were evidence of the increasingly urgent need to make up for the absence of properly conceived new designs by wringing the utmost development out of the obsolescent types with which the Luftwaffe had started the war.

Above: Capable of carrying two advanced LT 1b or LT F5b torpedoes, and Hohentwiel radar, the Ju 188E-2 was one of the best anti-shipping aircraft of World War II.

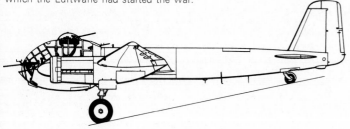

Above: The Ju 188A-2, a four-seat bomber with Jumo 213 engines boosted to 2,240hp each.

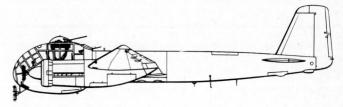

Above: Ju 188D-2 (shown in colour opposite).

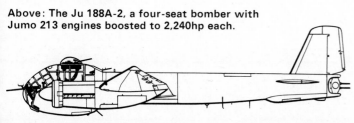

Above: The Ju 188C, with hydraulic tail barbette (abandoned).

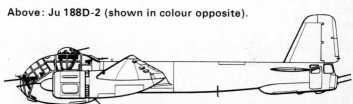

Above: Ju 188G-0 with wooden bomb pannier and manned turret.

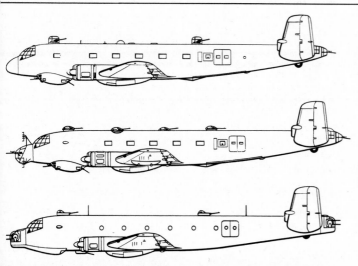

Above, from the top: Ju 290A-2, the first ocean patrol type; Ju 290A-8 with ten cannon; and the Ju 290B-1 heavy bomber.

Above: A rare air-to-air shot of the first Ju 290A-5 to be delivered to FAGr 5 ocean-reconnaissance geschwader in 1943.

Below: This picture of the first Ju 290A-3 (also used by 1/FAGr 5) shows the impressive size of these aircraft.

Messerschmitt Bf109

Bf 109B, C, D, E, F, G, H and K series, S-99 and 199, Ha-1109 and -1112

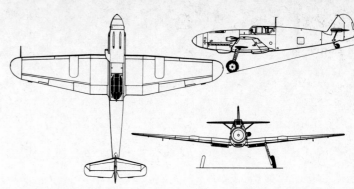

Origin: Bayerische Flugzeugwerke, later (1938) renamed Messerschmitt AG; very widely subcontracted throughout German-controlled territory and built under licence by Dornier-Werke, Switzerland, and Hispano-Aviación, Spain (post-war, Avia, Czechoslovakia).

Type: Single-seat fighter (many, fighter bomber).

Engine: (B, C) one 635hp Junkers Jumo 210D inverted-vee-12 liquid-cooled; (D) 1,000hp Daimler-Benz DB 600Aa, same layout; (E) 1,100hp DB 601A, 1,200hp DB 601N or 1,300hp DB 601E; (F) DB 601E; (G) 1,475hp DB 605A-1, or other sub-type up to DB 605D rated 1,800hp with MW50 boost; (H-1) DB 601E; (K) usually 1,550hp DB 605ASCM/DCM rated 2,000hp with MW50 boost; (S-199) 1,350hp Jumo 211F; (HA-1109) 1,300hp Hispano-Suiza 12Z-89 upright vee-12 or (M1L) 1,400hp R-R Merlin 500-45.

Dimensions: Span (A to E) 32ft 4½in (9·87m); (others) 32ft 6½in (9·92m); length (B, C) 27ft 11in; (D, E, typical) 28ft 4in (8·64m); (F) 29ft 0½in; (G) 29ft 8in (9·04m); (K) 29ft 4in; (HA-1109-M1L) 29ft 11in; height (E) 7ft 5½in (2·28m); (others) 8ft 6in (2·59m).

Weights: Empty (B-1) 3,483lb; (E) 4,189lb (1900kg) to 4,421lb; (F) around 4,330lb; (G) 5,880lb (2667kg) to 6,180lb (2800kg); (K, typical) 6,000lb; maximum loaded (B-1) 4,850lb; (E) 5,523lb (2505kg) to 5,875lb (2665kg); (F-3) 6,054lb; (G) usually 7,496lb (3400kg); (K) usually 7,439lb (3375kg).

Performance: Maximum speed (B-1) 292mph; (D) 323mph; (E) 348–354 mph (560–570km/h); (F-3) 390mph; (G) 353 to 428mph (569–690km/h), (K-4) 452mph (729km/h); initial climb (B-1) 2,200ft/min; (E) 3,100 to 3,280ft (1000m)/min; (G) 2,700 to 4,000ft/min; (K-4) 4,823ft (1470m)/min; service ceiling (B-1) 26,575ft; (E) 34,450ft (10,500m) to 36,090ft (11,000m); (F, G) around 38,000ft (11,600m); (K-4) 41,000ft (12,500m); range on internal fuel (all) 365–460 miles (typically, 700km).

Armament: (B) three 7·92mm Rheinmetall-Borsig MG 17 machine guns above engine and firing through propeller hub; (C) four MG 17, two above engine and two in wings, with fifth through propeller hub in C-2; (early E-1) four MG 17, plus four 50kg or one 250kg (551lb) bomb; (later E-1 and most other E) two MG 17 above engine, each with 1,000 rounds (or two MG 17 with 500 rounds, plus 20mm MG FF firing through propeller hub) and two MG FF in wings, each with 60-round drum; (F-1) two MG 17 and

Above: Abandoned high-altitude variant, the Bf 109H of 1944.

Below: The original prototype, with British Kestrel engine.

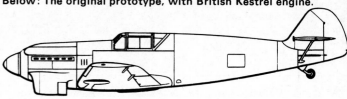

one MG FF; (F-2) two 15mm MG 151 and one MG FF; (F-4) two MG 151, one MG FF and one 20mm MG 151 in fairing under each wing; (G-1) two MG 17 or 13mm MG 131 over engine and one MG 151; (G-6) one 30mm MK 108, two MG 131 above engine and two MG 151 under wings; (K-4) two MG 151 above engine and one MK 108 or 103; (K-6) two MG 131 above engine, one MK 103 or 108 and two MK 108 under wings; (S-199) two MG 131 above engine and two MG 151 under wings; (HA-1109 series) two wing machine guns or 20mm Hispano 404. Many German G and K carried two 210mm rocket tubes under wings or various bomb loads.

History: First flight (Bf 109 V-1) early September 1935 (date is unrecorded); (production B-1) May 1937; (Bf 109E) January 1939; (Bf 109F prototype) July 1940; replacement in production by Bf 109G, May 1942.

Users: Bulgaria, Croatia, Finland, Germany (Luftwaffe), Hungary, Italy (ARSI), Japan, Jugoslavia, Romania, Slovakia, Slovak (CB Insurgent), Soviet Union (1940), Spain, Switzerland; (post-war) Czechoslovakia, Israel.

Above: Taken from a German propaganda film of 1941, this photograph depicts a pair of Bf 109E-4/Trop fighters of I/JG 27 flying over the Cyrenaican (Libyan) desert, soon after the entry of the Afrika Korps. Finish is 78 Light Blue, 79 Sand Yellow and 80 Olive Green, with the white tail band denoting the Mediterranean theatre of operations.

Above: One of the last Bf 109E sub-types, this is an E-7, seen with a large dust filter on the engine air inlet. It was operating on the Leningrad front in 1942 with JG 5.

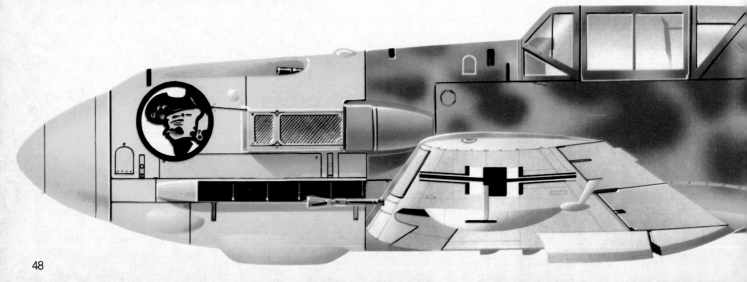

Above: The same I/JG 27 aircraft as seen at far left. This view from above flatters the camouflage capabilities of the 79/80 colour scheme against the North African terrain.

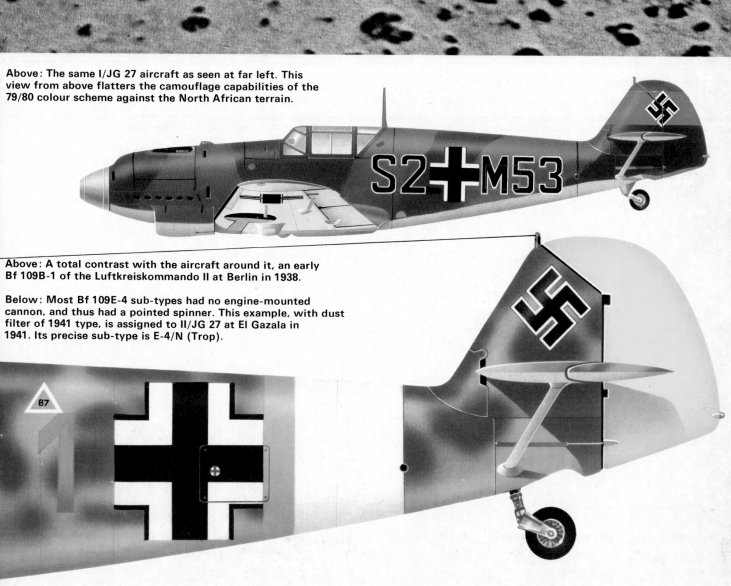

Above: A total contrast with the aircraft around it, an early Bf 109B-1 of the Luftkreiskommando II at Berlin in 1938.

Below: Most Bf 109E-4 sub-types had no engine-mounted cannon, and thus had a pointed spinner. This example, with dust filter of 1941 type, is assigned to II/JG 27 at El Gazala in 1941. Its precise sub-type is E-4/N (Trop).

Above: Bf 109G-2s of II (left) and III/JG 54 "Grunherz" (Green Heart) geschwader operating on the northern sector of the Eastern Front (probably at Silverskaya) in the summer of 1942. Relative merits of the Luftwaffe and Soviet fighters continue to be hotly debated.

Right: The Bf 109G-14/U4 introduced a wooden tail, previous improvements being the clear-view "Galland" hood and (five years late, and often incomplete) geared tabs on ailerons and/ or elevators.

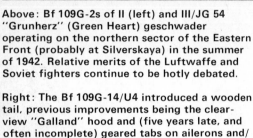

Messerschmitt Bf 109G-14/U4 cutaway drawing key:

1 Starboard navigation light
2 Starboard wingtip
3 Fixed trim tab
4 Starboard Frise-type aileron
5 Flush-riveted stressed wing-skinning
6 Handley Page leading-edge automatic slat
7 Slat control linkage
8 Slat equalizer rod
9 Aileron control linkage
10 Fabric-covered flap
11 Wheel fairing
12 Ammunition-feed fairing (both sides of fuselage)
13 Rheinmetall Borsig 13mm MG 131
14 Engine accessories
15 Starboard gun trough
16 Daimler-Benz DB 605AM twelve-cylinder inverted-vee liquid-cooled engine
17 Detachable cowling panel
18 Oil filler access
19 Oil tank
20 Propeller pitch-change mechanism
21 VDM electrically-operated constant-speed propeller
22 Spinner
23 Engine-mounted cannon muzzle
24 Blast tube
25 Propeller hub
26 Spinner back plate
27 Auxiliary cooling intakes
28 Coolant header tank
29 Anti-vibration rubber engine-mounting pads
30 Elektron forged engine bearer
31 Engine bearer support strut attachment
32 Plug leads
33 Exhaust manifold fairing strip
34 ejector exhausts
35 Cowling fasteners
36 Oil cooler
37 Oil cooler intake
38 Starboard mainwheel
39 Oil cooler outlet flap
40 Wing root fillet
41 Wing-fuselage fairing
42 Firewall/bulkhead
43 Supercharger air intake
44 Supercharger
45 20mm magazine
46 13mm ammunition feed
47 Engine bearer upper attachment
48 Ammunition feed fairing
49 MG 131 breeches
50 Instrument panel
51 20mm Mauser MG 151/20 cannon breech
52 Heel rests
53 Rudder pedals
54 Undercarriage emergency retraction cables
55 Fuselage frame

56 Wing/fuselage fairing
57 Undercarriage emergency retraction handwheel (outboard)
58 Tail trim handwheel (inboard)
59 Seat harness
60 Throttle lever
61 Control column
62 Cockpit ventilation inlet
63 Revi 16B reflector gunsight (folding)
64 Armoured windshield frame
65 Anti-glare gunsight screen
66 90mm armourglass wind-screen
67 'Galland'-type clear-vision hinged canopy
68 Framed armourglass head/back panel
69 Canopy contoured frame
70 Canopy hinges (starboard)
71 Canopy release catch
72 Pilot's bucket-type seat (8mm back armour)
73 Underfloor contoured fuel tank (88 gal/400 litres of 87 octane B4)
74 Fuselage frame

75 Circular access panel
76 Tail trimming cable conduit
77 Wireless leads
78 MW 50 (methanol water) tank (25 gal/114 litres capacity)
79 Handhold
80 Fuselage decking
81 Aerial mast
82 D/F loop
83 Oxygen cylinders (three)

84 Filler pipe
85 Wireless equipment packs (FuG 16zy communications and FuG 25a IFF)
86 Main fuel filler cap
88 Fuselage top keel (connector-stringer)
89 Aerial lead-in
90 Fuselage skin plating sections
91 'U' stringers
92 Fuselage frames (monocoque construction)
93 Tail trimming cables
94 Fin root fairing
95 Starboard fixed tailplane
96 Elevator balance
97 Starboard elevator
98 Geared elevator tab
99 All-wooden fin construction
100 Aerial attachment
101 Rudder upper hinge bracket
102 Rudder post
103 Fabric-covered wooden rudder structure
104 Geared rudder tab
105 Rear navigation light
106 Port elevator
107 Elevator geared tab

108 Tailplane structure
109 Rudder actuating linkage
110 Elevator control horn
111 Elevator connecting rod
112 Elevator control quadrant
113 Tailwheel leg cuff
114 Castoring non-retractable tailwheel
115 Lengthened tailwheel leg
116 Access panel
117 Tailwheel shock-strut
118 Lifting point
119 Rudder cable
120 Elevator cables
121 First-aid pack
122 Air bottles
123 Fuselage access panel
124 Bottom keel (connector stringer)
125 Ventral IFF aerial
126 Master compass
127 Elevator control linkage
128 Wing root fillet
129 Camber-changing flap
130 Ducted coolant radiator
131 Wing stringers
132 Wing rear pick-up point
133 Spar/fuselage upper pin joint (horizontal)

Development: During World War II the general public in the Allied nations at first regarded the Messerschmitt as an inferior weapon compared with the Spitfire and other Allied fighters. Only in the fullness of time was it possible to appreciate that the Bf 109 was one of the greatest combat aircraft in history. First flown in 1935, it was a major participant in the Spanish Civil War and a thoroughly proven combat aircraft by the time of Munich (September 1938). Early versions were the Bf 109B, C and D, all of lower power than the definitive 109E. The E was in service in great quantity by the end of August 1939 when the invasion of Poland began. From then until 1941 it was by far the most important fighter in the Luftwaffe, and it was also supplied in quantity to numerous other countries (which are listed above). During the first year of World War II the "Emil", as the various E sub-types were called, made mincemeat of the many and varied types of fighter against which it was opposed, with the single exception of the Spitfire (which it greatly outnumbered). Its good points were small size, fast and cheap production, high acceleration, fast climb and dive, and good power of manoeuvre. Nearly all 109Es were also fitted with two or three 20mm cannon, with range and striking power greater than a battery of eight rifle-calibre guns. Drawbacks were the narrow landing gear, severe swing on take-off or landing, extremely poor lateral control at high speeds, and the fact that in combat the slats on the wings often opened in tight turns; while this prevented a stall, it snatched at the ailerons and threw the pilot off his aim. After 1942 the dominant version was the 109G ("Gustav") which made up over 70 per cent of the total received by the Luftwaffe. Though formidably armed and equipped, the vast swarms of "Gustavs"

were nothing like such good machines as the lighter E and F, demanding constant pilot attention, constant high power settings, and having landing characteristics described as "malicious". Only a few of the extended-span high-altitude H-series were built, but from October 1944 the standard production series was the K with clear-view "Galland hood", revised wooden tail and minor structural changes. After World War II the Czech Avia firm found their Bf 109 plant intact and began building the S-99; running out of DB 605 engines they installed the slow-revving Jumo, producing the S-199 with even worse torque and swing than the German versions (pilots called it "Mezek" meaning mule), but in 1948 managed to sell some to Israel. The Spanish Hispano Aviación flew its first licence-built 1109 in March 1945 and in 1953 switched to the Merlin engine to produce the 1109-M1L Buchón (Pigeon). Several Hispano and Merlin versions were built in Spain, some being tandem-seat trainers. When the last HA-1112 flew out of Seville in late 1956 it closed out 21 years of manufacture of this classic fighter, during which total output approached 35,000.

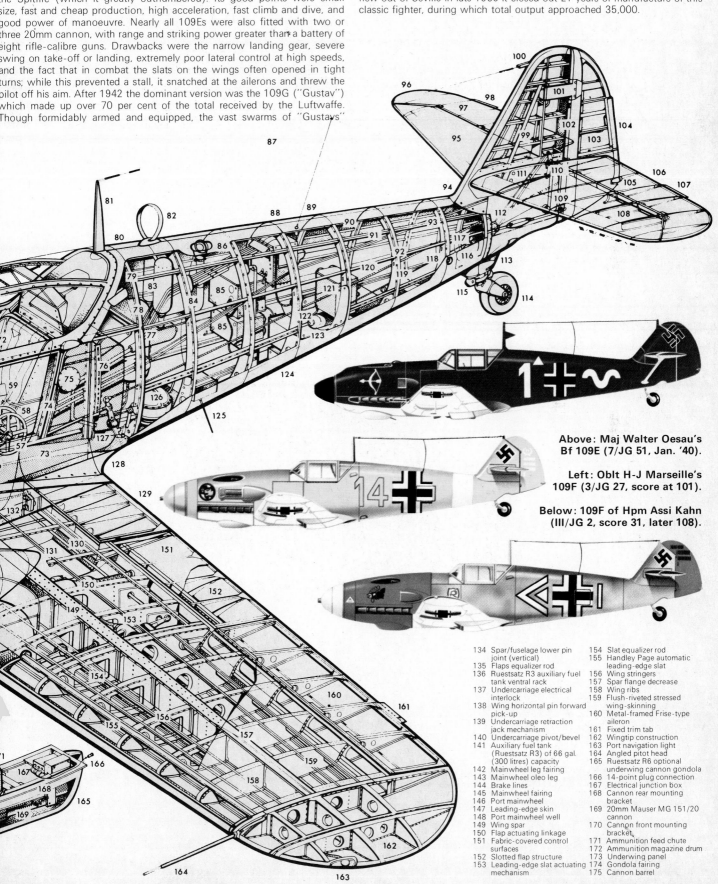

Above: Maj Walter Oesau's Bf 109E (7/JG 51, Jan. '40).

Left: Oblt H-J Marseille's 109F (3/JG 27, score at 101).

Below: 109F of Hpm Assi Kahn (III/JG 2, score 31, later 108).

134	Spar/fuselage lower pin joint (vertical)	
135	Flaps equalizer rod	
136	Ruestsatz R3 auxiliary fuel tank ventral rack	
137	Undercarriage electrical interlock	
138	Wing horizontal pin forward pick-up	
139	Undercarriage retraction jack mechanism	
140	Undercarriage pivot/bevel	
141	Auxiliary fuel tank (Ruestsatz R3) of 66 gal. (300 litres) capacity	
142	Mainwheel leg fairing	
143	Mainwheel oleo leg	
144	Brake lines	
145	Mainwheel fairing	
146	Port mainwheel	
147	Leading-edge skin	
148	Port mainwheel well	
149	Wing spar	
150	Flap actuating linkage	
151	Fabric-covered control surfaces	
152	Slotted flap structure	
153	Leading-edge slat actuating mechanism	
154	Slat equalizer rod	
155	Handley Page automatic leading-edge slat	
156	Wing stringers	
157	Spar flange decrease	
158	Wing ribs	
159	Flush-riveted stressed wing-skinning	
160	Metal-framed Frise-type aileron	
161	Fixed trim tab	
162	Wingtip construction	
163	Port navigation light	
164	Angled pitot head	
165	Ruestsatz R6 optional underwing cannon gondola	
166	14-point plug connection	
167	Electrical junction box	
168	Cannon rear mounting bracket	
169	20mm Mauser MG 151/20 cannon	
170	Cannon front mounting bracket	
171	Ammunition feed chute	
172	Ammunition magazine drum	
173	Underwing panel	
174	Gondola fairing	
175	Cannon barrel	

1: The Bf 109E-4B flown by Ltn Steindl, Geschwader-Adjutant of JG 54 "Grünherz", serving in the Leningrad area of the Eastern Front in the spring of 1942. Alongside is the emblem of II Gruppe, JG 54, the Vienna-Aspern coat of arms.

2: Bf 109E-1 of IV/JG 132, later redesignated I/JG 77, based at Werneuchen in early 1939, and the Gruppe's emblem.

3: The Bf 109 flown by Hpt Henschel, Gruppenkommandeur of II/JG 77, based at Aalborg, Norway, in July 1940. II/JG 77 landed in Norway on the second day of the invasion; the Gruppe's emblem is alongside.

4: Bf 109E-7B of II/SG 1, serving in the Stalingrad area in the winter of 1942-43, when, as the emblem indicates, the 109E had been restricted to the fighter-bomber and close-support roles.

5: Bf 109E-1 of II/JG 26 "Schlageter" at Düsseldorf in August 1939.

6: By August 1940 the various units of JG 26 had moved to France: this Bf 109E-3 was used by the Geschwader's 9. Staffel at Caffiers.

7: Bf 109E-1 of III/JG 52, based at Hopstädten in August 1940, with the Gruppe's "Winterfieldscher Wolf" emblem.

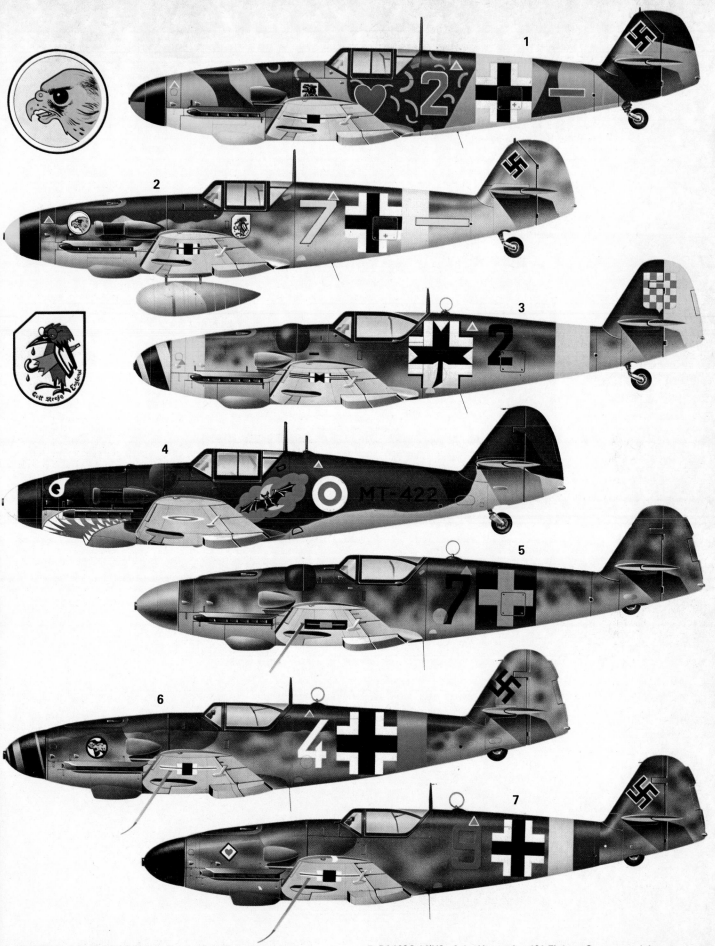

1: Bf 109G-2 of 4./JG 54 ''Grünherz'', based at Siverskaya, in the northern sector of the Eastern Front, in the summer of 1942.

2: Bf 109G-2/Trop of II/JG 51 ''Molders'' based at Casa Zeppera, Sardinia, in the summer of 1943, with the JG (above) and II Gruppe emblems.

3: Bf 109G-10/U4 operating with the kroat. Jagdstaffel under Jagdfliegerführer Ostpreussen at Eichwalde in November 1944.

4: Bf 109G-5/U2 in postwar service with the Finnish air force (HLeLv 31, based at Utti, in 1948).

5: Bf 109G-14/U2 of the Hungarian 101 Fighter Group, surviving elements of which were based in Austria in April 1945, following their withdrawal from home defence after the occupation of Hungary.

6: Bf 109K-4 of I/JG 27, based at Rheine, in December 1944. The K-series was intended to be the definitive production model of the 109, with minor modifications including the clear-view ''Galland'' hood and a pair of engine-mounted 15mm MG 151s in addition to the 30mm MK 108, but production did not begin until October 1944.

7: Bf 109K-4 of II/JG 77, based at Bönninghardt in December 1944.

Messerschmitt Bf 110

Bf 110B series to H series
(data for Bf 110C-4/B)

Origin: Bayerische Flugzeugwerke, after 1938 Messerschmitt AG; widely dispersed manufacture.

Type: Two-seat day and night fighter (also used on occasion for ground attack and reconnaissance).

Engines: Two 1,100hp Daimler-Benz DB 601A; (later C-4s) 1,200hp DB 601N 12-cylinder inverted-vee liquid-cooled; (G, H) two 1,475hp DB 605B, same layout.

Dimensions: Span 53ft 4¾in (16·25m); length 39ft 8½in (12·1m); height 11ft 6in (3·5m).

Weights: Empty 9,920lb (4500kg); loaded 15,430lb (7000kg).

Performance: Maximum speed 349mph (562km/h) at 22,966ft (7000m); climb to 18,045ft (5500m), 8 minutes; service ceiling 32,800ft (10,000m); range 528 miles (850km) at 304mph (490km/h) at 16,400ft (5000m).

Armament: Two 20mm Oerlikon MG FF cannon and four Rheinmetall 7·92mm MG 17 machine guns fixed firing forward in nose, one 7·92mm MG 15 manually aimed machine gun in rear cockpit; C-4/B also fitted with racks under centre section for four 551lb (250kg) bombs. (G-4 night

Above: Bf 110D of 8/ZG 26 climbing out of rugged territory in Sicily in 1942 to rendezvous with a bomber force for Malta.

Messerschmitt Bf 110G-4b/R3 cutaway drawing key:

1 The Hirschgeweih (Stag's Antlers) array for the FuG 220b Lichtenstein SN-2 radar
2 Single-pole type antenna for the FuG 212 Lichtenstein C-1 radar
3 Camera gun
4 Cannon muzzles
5 Cannon ports
6 Blast tubes
7 Starboard mainwheel
8 Armour plate (10-mm)
9 Twin 30-mm Rheinmetall Borsig MK 108 (Rüstsatz/Field Conversion Set 3) with 135 rpg
10 Armoured bulkhead
11 Supercharger intake
12 Position of nacelle-mounted instruments on day fighter model
13 Exhaust flame damper
14 Auxiliary tank
15 Three-blade VDM airscrew
16 Leading-edge automatic slat
17 Pitot tube
18 FuG 227/1 Flensburg homing aerial fitted to some aircraft by forward maintenance units (to home on Monica tail-warning radar emissions)
19 Stressed wing skinning
20 Starboard aileron
21 Trim tab
22 Slotted flap
23 Hinged canopy roof
24 Armoured glass windscreen (60-mm)
25 Instrument panel
26 Cockpit floor armour (4-mm)
27 Twin 20-mm Mauser MG 151 cannon with 300 rounds (port) and 350 rounds (starboard)
28 Pilot's seat
29 Control column
30 Pilot's back and head armour (8-mm)
31 Cannon magazine
32 Centre section carry-through
33 Radar operator's swivel seat
34 D/F loop
35 Aerial mast
36 Upward-firing cannon muzzles
37 Two 30-mm MK 108 cannon in schräge Musik (oblique music) installation firing obliquely upward (optional installation supplied as an Umrüst-Bausatz/Factory Conversion Set)
38 Ammunition drums
39 Aft cockpit bulkhead
40 FuG 10P HF R/T set
41 FuB1 2F airfield blind approach receiver
42 Handhold
43 Oxygen bottles
44 Aerials
45 Master compass
46 Starboard tailfin
47 Rudder balance
48 Rudder
49 Tab
50 Starboard elevator
51 Starboard tailplane
52 Variable-incidence tailplane
53 Elevator tab
54 Centre section fairing
55 Rear navigation light
56 Port elevator
57 Port tailfin
58 Rudder
59 Hinged tab
60 Tailwheel
61 Fuselage frames
62 Control lines
63 Dipole tuner
64 Batteries
65 Transformer
66 Slotted flap
67 Fuel tank of 57·3 Imp gal (260·5l) capacity
68 Oil tank of 7·7 Imp gal (35l) capacity
69 Ventral antenna
70 Coolant radiator
71 Radiator intake
72 Hinged intake fairing
73 Aileron tab
74 Aileron construction
75 Wingtip
76 Flensburg aerial (see
77 Port navigation light
78 Leading-edge automa slat
79 Wing ribs
80 Mainspar
81 Underwing auxiliary f tank (66-Imp gal/300 capacity)
82 Landing light
83 Undercarriage door
84 Mainwheel well
85 Supercharger intake
86 Undercarriage pivot p
87 Mainwheel leg
88 Mainwheel
89 Oil cooler
90 Oil cooler intake
91 VDM airscrew

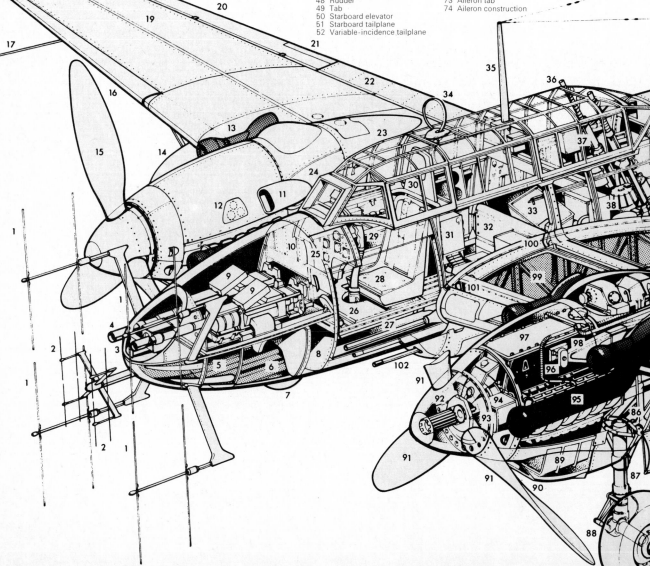

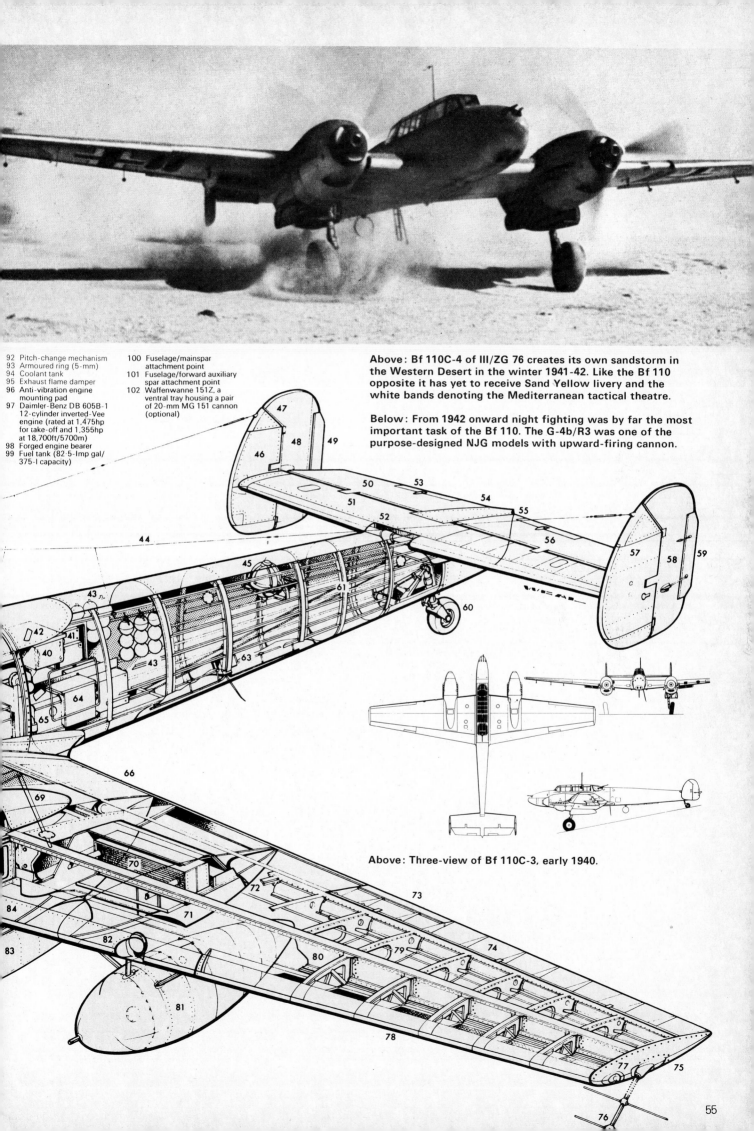

92 Pitch-change mechanism
93 Armoured ring (5-mm)
94 Coolant tank
95 Exhaust flame damper
96 Anti-vibration engine mounting pad
97 Daimler-Benz DB 605B-1 12-cylinder inverted-Vee engine (rated at 1,475hp for take-off and 1,355hp at 18,700ft/5700m)
98 Forged engine bearer
99 Fuel tank (82·5-Imp gal/ 375-I capacity)

100 Fuselage/mainspar attachment point
101 Fuselage/forward auxiliary spar attachment point
102 Waffenwanne 151Z, a ventral tray housing a pair of 20-mm MG 151 cannon (optional)

Above: Bf 110C-4 of III/ZG 76 creates its own sandstorm in the Western Desert in the winter 1941-42. Like the Bf 110 opposite it has yet to receive Sand Yellow livery and the white bands denoting the Mediterranean tactical theatre.

Below: From 1942 onward night fighting was by far the most important task of the Bf 110. The G-4b/R3 was one of the purpose-designed NJG models with upward-firing cannon.

Above: Three-view of Bf 110C-3, early 1940.

► fighter) two 30mm MK 108 and two 20mm MG 151 firing forward, and two MG 151 in Schräge Musik installation firing obliquely upwards (sometimes two 7·92mm MG 81 in rear cockpit).

History: First flight (Bf 110V1 prototype) 12 May 1936; (pre-production Bf 110C-0) February 1939; operational service with Bf 110C-1, April 1939; final run-down of production (Bf 110H-2 and H-4) February 1945.

User: Germany (Luftwaffe).

Development: As in five other countries at about the same time, the Reichsluftfahrtministerium decided in 1934 to issue a requirement for a new kind of fighter having two engines and exceptional range. Called a Zerstörer (destroyer), it was to be as capable as small single-seaters of fighting other aircraft, possibly making up in firepower for any lack in manoeuvrability. Its dominant quality was to be range, to escort bombers on raids penetrating deep into enemy heartlands. Powered by two of the new DB 600 engines, the prototype reached 316mph, considered an excellent speed, but it was heavy on the controls and unimpressive in power of manoeuvre. Too late to be tested in the Spanish Civil War, the production Bf 110B-1, which was the first to carry the two cannon, was itself supplanted by the C-series with the later DB 601 engine with direct fuel injection and greater power at all heights. By the start of World War II the Luftwaffe had 195 Bf 110C fighters, and in the Polish campaign these were impressive, operating mainly in the close-support role but demolishing any aerial opposition they encountered. It was the same story in the Blitzkrieg war through the Low Countries and France, when 350 of the big twins were used. Only when faced with RAF Fighter Command in the Battle of Britain did the Bf 110 suddenly prove a disaster. It was simply no match for the Spitfire or even the Hurricane, and soon the Bf 109 was having to escort the escort fighters! But production of DB 605-powered versions, packed with radar and night-fighting equipment, was actually trebled in 1943 and sustained in 1944, these G and H models playing a major part in the night battles over the Reich in 1943–45.

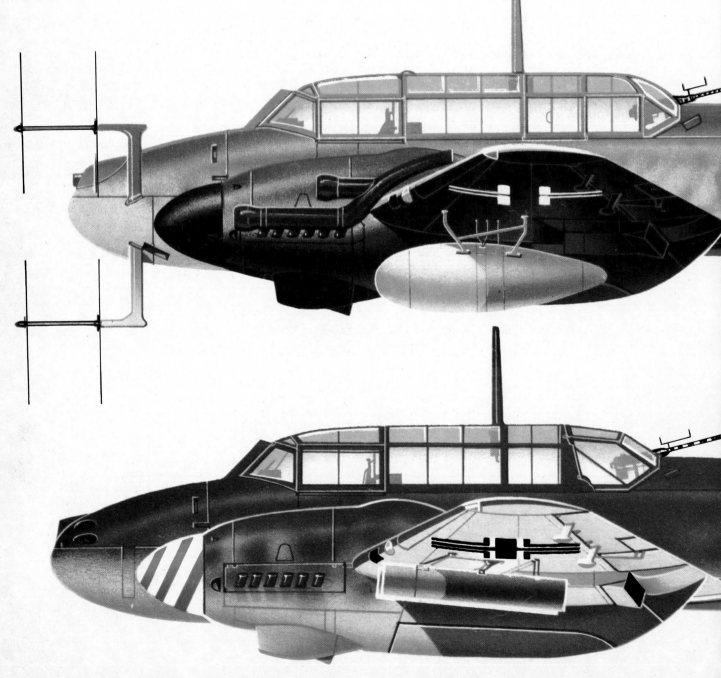

Above left: An unidentified trio of what appear to be Bf 110Ds reveal little beyond the staffel colour of yellow seen on the tips of the spinners. They are probably from 9/ZG, newly assigned to the North African theatre.

Above: A pair of Bf 110D-1s airborne over the Mediterranean in 1941. These aircraft are from ZG 26, and are wearing Sand Yellow with white North African theatre bands on the rear fuselage.

Above: A typical Luftwaffe night fighter of the late war period was this Bf 110G-4 of 7/NJG 4 based at many airfields in northwest Germany as well as St Trond and Venlo in the Netherlands. Finished in 76 Light Blue all over, the upper surfaces were then given a sprayed mottle of 75 Grey-violet.

Below: A day-flying DB 605-powered version, a Bf 110G-2 of 5/ZG 76, based at Grossenhain in the winter of 1943-44. In happier days in 1939-41, ZG 76 had been the original Haifisch unit, with prominent shark mouths to its aircraft noses.

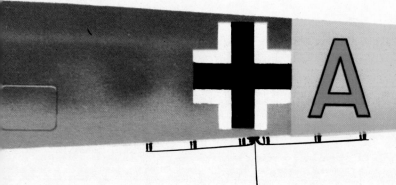

Messerschmitt Me 163 Komet

Me 163B-1

Origin: Messerschmitt AG.
Type Single-seat interceptor.
Engine: One 3,750lb (1700kg) thrust Walter HWK 509A-2 bi-propellant rocket burning concentrated hydrogen peroxide (T-stoff) and hydrazine/methanol (C-stoff).
Dimensions: Span 30ft 7in (9·3m); length 18ft 8in (5·69m); height 9ft 0in (2·74m).
Weights: Empty 4,191lb (1905kg); loaded 9,042lb (4110kg).
Performance: Maximum speed 596mph (960km/h) at 32,800ft (10,000m); initial climb 16,400ft (5000m)/min; service ceiling 54,000ft (16,500m); range depended greatly on flight profile but under 100km (62 miles); endurance 2½min from top of climb or eight min total.
Armament: Two 30mm MK 108 cannon in wing roots, each with 60 rounds.
History: First flight (Me 163V1) spring 1941 as glider, August 1941 under power; (Me 163B) August 1943; first operational unit (I/JG400) May 1944.
User: Germany (Luftwaffe).

Development: Of all aircraft engaged in World War II the Me 163 Komet (Comet) was the most radical and, indeed, futuristic. The concept of the short-endurance local-defence interceptor powered by a rocket engine was certainly valid and might have been more of a thorn in the Allies' side

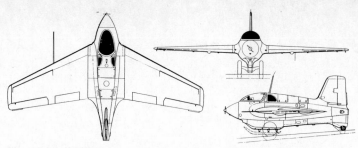

Above: Me 163B-1a showing takeoff trolley and landing skid.

than it was. Even the dramatically unconventional form of the Me 163, with no horizontal tail and an incredibly short fuselage, did not lead to great difficulty; in fact, the production fighter was widely held to have the best and safest characteristics of any aircraft in the Luftwaffe. But the swift strides into uncharted technology were bold in the extreme. It was partly to save weight and drag that the tailless configuration was adopted, and partly because the moving spirit behind the project was at first Dr Alex Lippisch,

Below: Purging the propellant pipes, with C-stoff generating steam clouds. On the ground the Komet was extremely dangerous!

Below: The prototype Me 163A V1 (first prototype), which languished 18 months as a glider before its rocket was fitted.

Messerschmitt Me 210 and 410 Hornisse

Me 210A, B and C series, Me 410A and B series

Origin: Messerschmitt AG.
Type: Two-seat tactical aircraft for fighter, attack and reconnaissance duties with specialised variants.
Engines: (Me 210, usual for production versions) two 1,395hp Daimler-Benz DB 601F inverted-vee-12 liquid-cooled; (Me 410A series, usual for production versions) two 1,750hp DB 603A of same layout; (Me 410B series) two 1,900hp DB 603G.
Dimensions: Span (210) 53ft 7¼in, later 53ft 7¾in (16·4m); (410) 53ft 7¾in; length (without 50mm gun, radar or other long fitment) (210) 40ft 3in (12·22m); (410) 40ft 10in or 40ft 11½in (12·45m); height (both) 14ft 0½in (4·3m).
Weights: Empty (210A) about 12,000lb (5440kg); (410A-1) 13,560lb (6150kg); maximum loaded (210A-1) 17,857lb (8100kg); (410A-1) 23,483lb (10,650kg).
Performance: Maximum speed (both, clean) 385mph (620km/h); initial climb (both) 2,133ft (650m)/min; service ceiling (210A-1) 22,967ft (7000m); (410A-1) 32,800ft (10,000m); range with full bomb load (210A-1) 1,491 miles (2400km); (410A-1) 1,447 miles (2330km).
Armament: Varied, but basic aircraft invariably defended by two remotely-controlled powered barbettes on sides of fuselage each housing one 13mm MG 131 and, if bomber version, provided with internal weapon bay housing two 1,102lb (500kg) bombs; external racks on nearly all (210 and 410) for two 1,102lb stores (exceptionally, two 2,204lb). Normal fixed forward-firing armament of two 20mm MG 151/20 and two 7·92mm MG 17. Me 410 versions had many kinds of bomber-destroyer armament, as described in the text.
History: First flight (Me 210V-1) 2 September 1939; (pre-production 210A-0) April 1941; final delivery (210) April 1942; first flight (310) 11 September 1943; (410V-1) probably December 1942.
User: Germany (Luftwaffe).

Development: Planned in 1937 as a valuable and more versatile successor to the Bf 110 twin-engined escort fighter, the Me 210 was little more than a flop and made hardly any contribution to the German war effort. After severe flight instability and landing-gear problems some progress was made in 1941 towards producing an acceptable machine which could be put into

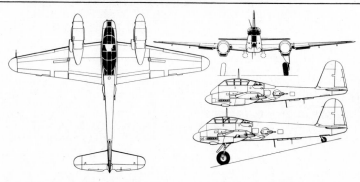

Above: Three-view of Me 210A-2 (upper side view, A-0).

Right: This Messerschmitt Me 410A-3 Hornisse was captured by the RAF at Trapani in Sicily in 1943. Previously operated by 2.(F)/122, it was one of the specialized photo-reconnaissance variants with a deepened forward fuselage without an internal weapons bay to allow the installation of two Rb 20/30, 50/30 or 75/30 cameras.

Below: Another A-3 showing the deep fuselage. Previous photo-reconnaissance versions of the Me 410 Hornisse had been mere lash-ups, with the cameras inadequately installed in the bomb bay and giving extremely poor results.

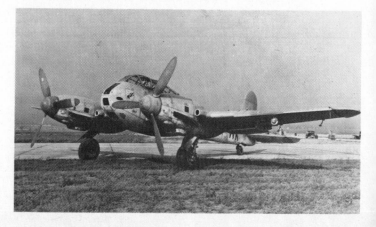

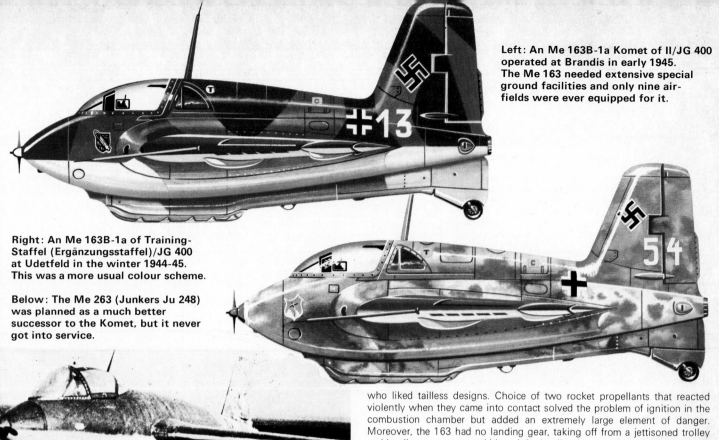

Left: An Me 163B-1a Komet of II/JG 400 operated at Brandis in early 1945. The Me 163 needed extensive special ground facilities and only nine airfields were ever equipped for it.

Right: An Me 163B-1a of Training-Staffel (Ergänzungsstaffel)/JG 400 at Udetfeld in the winter 1944-45. This was a more usual colour scheme.

Below: The Me 263 (Junkers Ju 248) was planned as a much better successor to the Komet, but it never got into service.

who liked tailless designs. Choice of two rocket propellants that reacted violently when they came into contact solved the problem of ignition in the combustion chamber but added an extremely large element of danger. Moreover, the 163 had no landing gear, taking off from a jettisoned trolley and landing on a sprung skid, and the landing impact often sloshed residual propellants together causing a violent explosion. Many aircraft were lost this way, and the original test pilot, glider champion Heini Dittmar, was badly injured when the skid failed to extend. Nevertheless by 1944 these bat-like specks were swooping on US bomber formations with devastating effect. Numerous improved versions were flying at VE day, but only 370 Komets had seen service and these had suffered high attrition through accidents.

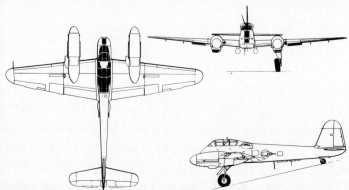

Above: Three-view of Me 410A-1 Hornisse (Hornet).

production against the order for 1,000 placed "off the drawing board" in June 1939. Accidents were nevertheless frequent and manufacture was terminated at the 352nd aircraft. This major blow to the Luftwaffe and the company, which was reflected in an official demand for Willi Messerschmitt's resignation from the board, was partly salvaged by a further redesign and change to the DB 603 engine. The Me 310 was a high-altitude fighter-bomber with 58ft 9in wing and pressure cabin, but this was abandoned in favour of a less radical change designated 410. As with the 210, the reconnaissance 410s usually had cameras in the bomb bay and no MG 17s, while some attack or destroyer versions had four forward-firing MG 151 cannon, or two MG 151 and a 50mm BK 5 gun with 21 rounds. The Me 410A-2/U-2 was an important night fighter with SN-2 Lichtenstein radar and two MG 151 and two 30mm MK 108. Many of the 1,121 Me 410s carried Rüstsatz external packs housing two more MG 151, MK 108 or MK 103, and occasionally experienced pilots fitted as many as eight MG 151 all firing ahead. The 210mm rocket tube was a common fitment by 1944, some aircraft having a rotating pack of six tubes in the bomb bay.

Messerschmitt Me 262

Me 262A-1a Schwalbe, Me 262A-2 Sturmvogel, Me 262B-1a

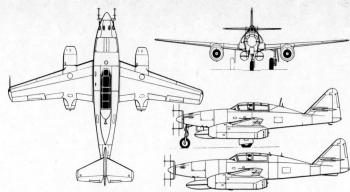

Origin: Messerschmitt AG.
Type: (A-1a) single-seat fighter, (A-2a) single-seat bomber, (262B-1a) two-seat night fighter.
Engines: Two 1,980lb (900kg) thrust Junkers Jumo 004B single-shaft axial turbojets.
Dimensions: Span 40ft 11½in (12·5m); length 34ft 9½in (10·6m), (262B-1a, excluding radar aerials) 38ft 9in (11·8m); height 12ft 7in (3·8m).
Weights: Empty (A-1a, A-2a) 8,820lb (4000kg); (B-1a) 9,700lb (4400kg); loaded (A-1a, A-2a) 15,500lb (7045kg); (B-1a) 14,110lb (6400kg).
Performance: Maximum speed (A-1a) 540mph (870km/h); (A-2a, laden) 470mph (755km/h); (B-1a) 497mph (800km/h); initial climb (all) about 3,940ft (1200m)/min; service ceiling 37,565ft (11,500m); range on internal fuel, at altitude, about 650 miles (1050km).
Armament: (A-1a) four 30mm MK 108 cannon in nose, two with 100 rounds each, two with 80; (A-1a/U1) two 30mm MK 103, two MK 108 and two 20mm MG 151/20; (A-1b) as A-1a plus 24 spin-stabilised R4/M 50mm rockets; (B-1a) as A-1a; (B-2a) as A-1a plus two inclined MK 108 behind cockpit in Schräge Musik installation; (D) SG 500 Jagdfaust with 12 rifled mortar barrels inclined in nose; (E) 50mm MK 114 gun or 48 R4/M rockets; bomb load of two 1,100lb (500kg) bombs carried by A-2a.
History: First flight (262V1 on Jumo 210 piston engine) 4 April 1941; (262V3 on two Jumo 004-0 turbojets) 18 July 1942; (Me 262A-1a) 7 June 1944; first delivery (A-0 to Rechlin) May 1944; first experimental combat unit (EK 262) 30 June 1944; first regular squadron (8/ZG26) September 1944.
User: Germany (Luftwaffe).

Development: In the Me 262 the German aircraft industry created a potentially war-winning aircraft which could have restored to the Luftwaffe command of the skies over Germany. Compared with Allied fighters of its day, including the RAF Meteor I, which entered service a little earlier, it was much faster and packed a much heavier punch. Radar-equipped night fighter versions and sub-types designed to stand off from large bomber formations and blast them out of the sky were also developments against which the Allies had no answer. Yet for years the programme was held back by official disinterest, and by the personal insistence of Hitler that the world-beating jet should be used only as a bomber! It was in the autumn of 1938 that Messerschmitt was asked to study the design of a jet fighter, and the resulting Me 262 was remarkably unerring. First flown on a piston engine in the nose, it then flew on its twin turbojets and finally, in July 1943, the fifth development aircraft flew with a nosewheel. Despite numerous snags, production aircraft were being delivered in July 1944 and the rate of production was many times that of the British Meteor. On the other hand the

Above: Three-view of the Me 262B-1a night fighter; lower side view, the longer B-2a specially designed for this role.

Above: Starting the Jumo 004B engines of an A-1a of the Kommando Nowotny in late October 1944 (probably at Achmer). The Me 262 was potentially the greatest fighter of the war.

German axial engines were unreliable and casualties due to engine failure, fires or break-up were heavy. The MK 108 gun was also prone to jam, and the landing gear to collapse. Yet the 262 was a beautiful machine to handle and, while Allied jets either never reached squadrons or never engaged enemy aircraft, the 100 or so Me 262s that flew on operations and had fuel available destroyed far more than 100 Allied bombers and fighters. Even more remarkable, by VE-day total deliveries of this formidable aircraft reached 1,433.

Messerschmitt Me 321 and 323 Gigant

Me 321A and B, Me 323D and E

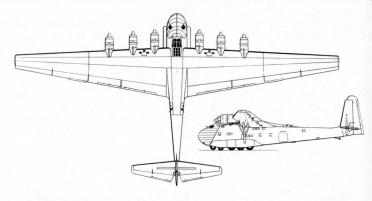

Origin: Messerschmitt AG.
Type: (321) heavy cargo glider; (323) heavy cargo transport.
Engines: (321) none; (323 production variants) six 1,140hp Gnome-Rhône 14N 48/49 14-cylinder two-row radials.
Dimensions: Span 180ft 5½in (55m); length 92ft 4¼in (28·15m); height (321B-1) 33ft 3½in (10·15m); (323) 31ft 6in (9·6m).
Weights: Empty (321B-1) 27,432lb (12,400kg); (323D-6) 60,260lb (27,330kg); (323E-1) 61,700lb (28,010kg); maximum loaded (321B-1) 75,852lb (34,400kg); (323D-6) 94,815lb (43,000kg); (323E-1) 99,208lb (45,000kg).
Performance: Maximum speed (321 on tow) 99mph (160km/h); (323D series) 177mph (285km/h); initial climb (321 towed by three Bf 110) 492ft (150m)/min; (323D series) 710ft (216m)/min; service ceiling (323D) about 13,100ft (4000m); range with "normal" payload (presumably not maximum) 684 miles (1100km).
Armament: See text.
History: First flight (321V-1) 7 March 1941; service delivery (321) about June 1941; final delivery (321) April 1942; first flight (323V-1) some reports claim April 1941 but others, much more plausible, state "autumn 1941"; service delivery (323D-1) May 1942; final delivery March 1944.
User: Germany (Luftwaffe).

Development: Following the dramatic vindication of the previously untried Blitzkrieg concept of airborne forces in May 1940 the Reichsluftfahrtministerium (RLM) asked Junkers and Heinkel to design huge transport gliders far bigger than the little DFS 230 used in the invasion of the Benelux countries. Junkers' Ju 322 Mammut was an expensive failure, but

Above: Two-view of the Me 323D-1, the most numerous version.

Right: Man-handling an artillery piece, probably a 75mm Pak.40 anti-tank gun, up into the hold of an Me 323D-1.

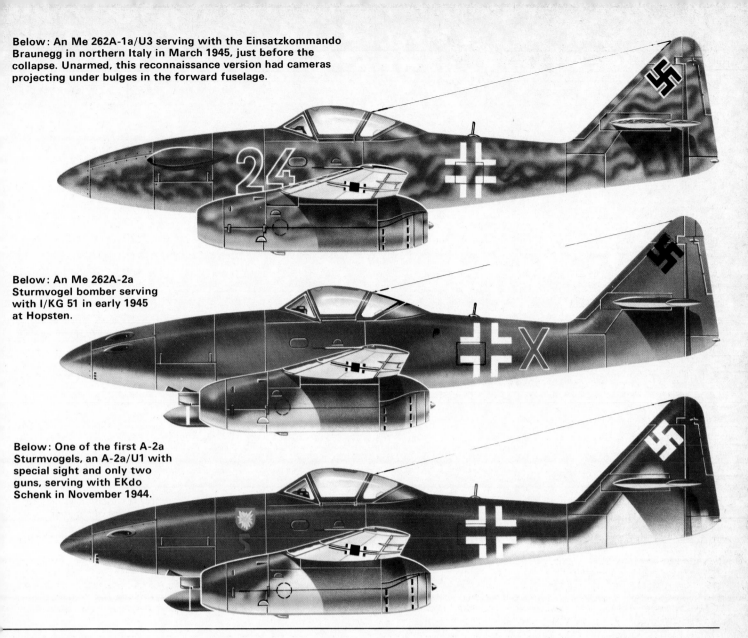

Below: An Me 262A-1a/U3 serving with the Einsatzkommando Braunegg in northern Italy in March 1945, just before the collapse. Unarmed, this reconnaissance version had cameras projecting under bulges in the forward fuselage.

Below: An Me 262A-2a Sturmvogel bomber serving with I/KG 51 in early 1945 at Hopsten.

Below: One of the first A-2a Sturmvogels, an A-2a/U1 with special sight and only two guns, serving with EKdo Schenk in November 1944.

the Me 321 Gigant went into production, despite the fact it was extremely tiring to fly on account of the very high control forces needed. Made chiefly of welded steel tube, with plywood or fabric covering, it carried the large payload of 48,500lb (22 tonnes), or a company of infantry. The 321A-1 had a single pilot but most of the 175 built were 321B-1 with a pair of crew who served as navigator and radio operator and manned two twin 7·92mm MG 15 machine guns in beam windows. Usual towing scheme was three Bf 110 in formation, but the specially built He 111Z was preferable and many units used various arrangements of take-off boost rockets. Dipl-Ing Degel then studied the powered 321C and D and eventually these became the 323V-1 with four engines (complete nacelles already in production at SNCASO for the Bloch 175) and 323V-2 with six. The six-engined Gigant

went into production, the D-1 having three-blade metal propellers and the D-2 two-blade wooden, each having five MG 15 in the nose and mounts for six MG 34 infantry m.g. in beam windows. Most later had five 13mm MG 131 added, but this did not stop Beaufighters shooting 14 into the sea as they ferried petrol to Rommel. Final versions in the run of 210 were the E-series with 1,340hp Jumo 211F, the E-1 having an MG 151 20mm turret above each centre-engine nacelle, and the 323G with 1,320hp Gnome-Rhône 14R.

Below: Takeoff of an Me 321A-1 Gigant under the lusty pull of a Heinkel He 111Z five-engined tug. The Z could handle the monster glider without the latter needing a.t.o. rockets.